Just
a moment,
GOD!

Just a moment, God!

An anthology of Verse and Prose from East Africa

Edited by
ROBERT GREEN

EAST AFRICAN LITERATURE BUREAU

Nairobi   Kampala   Dar es Salaam

EAST AFRICAN LITERATURE BUREAU

P.O. Box 30022 Nairobi
P.O. Box 1317 Kampala
P.O. Box 1408 Dar es Salaam

CONTENTS

Part I

VERSE

Part II

PROSE

CONTENTS

Part 1
VERSE

AKBAR KHAN was born in India in 1939 and educated at a Catholic Missionary School before going to Karnatak University for his B.A. and M.A. degrees. He came to Tanzania in 1967 and is now teaching in a Secondary School in Dar es Salaam. The first of his two poems printed here, *Just a Moment, God*, is marked by the poet's confident manipulation of the rhythms of spoken English in his exploration of the theme of God's inhumanity. In the second poem, *Marlowe*, the revolutionary Elizabethan poet and dramatist, Christopher Marlowe—author of *The Jew of Malta*, *Dr. Faustus* and *Tamburlaine*—powerfully tells us of his own philosophy of life. Both these poems are linked by Khan's interest in the relationship between life and a religious belief.

Just a moment, God!

O God Almighty, as you are called,
Who sit ever-watchful above us all,
Or, which is more probable, sleep
Supinely in your ethereal abode
Which is neither here nor there, and yet
They say, is everywhere (whatever that means)—
Please turn aside from your stupendous task
Of moulding galaxies and polishing up suns,
Knocking down sparrows, decomposing dead leaves,
And benevolently scattering your largesse of
    misery here below,
And listen to what one of your insignificant
    creatures has to say.

Others adore you, god, but I prefer to laugh at you.

Men have fashioned you in many forms,
But you were fashioned best in stone, god.
Yes, your true substance is stone—cold, immovable,
    finished!

For, god, what do you know of human feelings?

3

Look—
Have you ever felt the clammy fingers of fear
Squeezing and squeezing you, while the world around
Whispered and rocked in panic?
Or lain awake on blank endless nights, weeping
softly

For things that can never be the way you want them?
Have you, in a dizzy spell, seen
The darkness gathering around you in clamorous
beats of sound
And said, "Perhaps this is death; how beautiful
is death?"

Have you ever held a book in your hand
And heard your heart keeping time with one
Who, though dead and gone ages ago,
Opposed your most cowardly invention death
With nothing more forbidding than a mere quill?
And have you walked on golden days
Under unforgettable skies by the side of her,
Who, with the laughter of her eyes, the radiance
of her face,

Could make your heaven seem superfluous?
You may be all mighty, all wise and all that, god,
But you never were,
Nor ever could be
A Man.
I pity you.

Marlowe

Hurling wordy thunders
I dumbstrike sorry humanity,
Daring to live as I dared to believe.
Alone among an age
I rage at myths, grapple with firm-forged bonds
That seek to trammel my soaring days.
My *Jew*, my *Faust*, my *Tamburlaine*
Are each me, each only me, set free
From the cramping limits of this corporeal rag,
Fit at all times for the gaping earth.
No matter,—whilst I live, I live.
But when death comes, bid me goodnight,
For no other morrow dawns than this:
The only one the human soul can know.

FRANCIS BARASA has five poems at the beginning of this book (see pp. 6–13) and has also contributed six of his stories to this collection: *The Will of God*; *Christmas Day*; *Back Home*; *Things Take the Wrong Course*; *The Hooting Owl*; and, finally, *Pride and Prejudice*. The first story, *The Will of God*, is a black and macabre account of the tragedies that befall a poor Muslim family living a precarious existence in a city shack: for this family there seems to be no escape from a merciless fate. *Christmas Day*, in contrast, is set in a Kikuyu village and recounts the mixture of comedy and near-tragedy in the events accompanying a Christmas feast; these events precipitate a change in the relationship between a son and his father which is delicately described at the end of the story. Barasa's third story, *Back Home*, re-echoes a theme that is common to much contemporary East African writing: the clash between the values of the town and those of the unwesternised village. This story is memorable both for its description of the confrontation in the mind of its young Masai hero, and for the vivid picture that is drawn of the boy's lonely journey through Masailand. *Things Take the Wrong Course* in Barasa's next story because the power of the old rain-maker has been challenged by the white Christian missionary. Mwangi therefore decides to invoke his gods to stop the rains. The story ends ironically and surprisingly. *The Hooting Owl* is also set in Kikuyuland and describes a young boy's fearful state of mind after the mysterious disappearance of his grandfather. Finally, and in a completely different mood, *Pride and Prejudice* is a lyrical account of the courtship of a great warrior and the daughter of a despised thief; and how the warrior's father is persuaded to change his mind and allow his son to marry the daughter of a degraded man.

Growth

The sun took to its course
And slowly, reverently
Coursed along the brilliant path of peace—

> To and fro;
> Coming and going;
> Day in, day out:
> Uncountable times—

To its unknown destination yonder.
And with each journey, I sprouted;
I grew and matured.
And the world grew as I grew
And knew what I knew.

F. N. BARASA

My mother died

She came early in the morning to the river
With her precious gourd in her hands
   To draw water—
Water to wash her only, dear son's eyes,
But, with her gourd, she drew death
   From the river.

For the croc, an early riser, a fierce monster,
Was waiting ravenously to feed on her—
To feed on the body of my dear mother.

When she bended, with her gourd in her hands
So as to reach the warm, gurgling water,
The croc shot out like fire-sparks.
It whirled its calloused, strong tail—
Its deadly weapon which never did fail
   it before—
And threw my mother and her gourd
Into the river and then dragged her
Down, down, deep to the kingdom of the river-god.

She screamed with womanly fear
And cried with motherly love,
But I was not there to hear,
Even then I was but a baby—
Too young to save her body.
At home I missed her and cried—
Long, shrieking piteable cries
Of a baby hungry for mother's breasts
But she never, never came back;
My mother never again came back!

It is here, near the banks of this river
   Where she died.
It is into this hypocritical river
   That she vanished.

She left me empty, naked
And unwashed.

And I know that long as I live
I shall remain unwashed.
For who else's hands can wash me clean
And remove that dirt she left that morn?

Welcome, New Year

"Goodbye, goodbye, old year"
And

"Welcome, welcome, new year".
So we sang in chorus together,
A hired, overdone grin
Stuck to our wet, flabby lips
—Pretending that we are happy
For a new something.

"Welcome, new year"

Has come;
Every new something is likeable
Indeed.

"Welcome, new year!"

The last line in our diary
Is gone;
Another line, new one, with each singing of
"Welcome, new year",
Will be waiting.

An old leaf has wilted and died with each
"Welcome, new year",
While a new one is sprouting, healthy
And gaily at the top.

"Goodbye, old year!"
"Welcome, new year!"—with a grim smile
And tears pricking my old eyes
For it revives in me
The good old memories—
    The good, gone times I had;

It hurts to see that leaf
Wilt and weakly die.

I was ninety a while ago
And ninety-one now with the
"Welcome, new year".

My eyelids are falling
And my ears are failing,
Without being told, I know;
I am the last line in the diary,
The old, weak leaf at the bottom.

—Yes, I am wilting now, and with the
"Welcome, new year"
I know I am done
For a new one has sprouted at the top
    To reign after me.

F. N. BARASA

The warrior's love

Like a sacred tree he stood,
Unconcerned with the world
And alone;
Yet among his friends,
His brothers and his parents.

His spear and club in hand,
And a bow—not to mention the sword—
Erect he stood
With the pride of an acclaimed hero:

    The guardian of peace and glory,
    The symbol of pride and envy.

Yet with these hard-earned titles
After countless fought-and-won battles
He never could achieve happiness,
He never was at peace with the world.

His fellow heroes talked to him
And, tired, disheartened, away they went;
His mother, worried about him,
Bitterly, painfully wept.

But never could they soften his heart;
Never could her tears moisten his heart.

And like a holy tree
He stood alone
And cast his eyes
Upon the horizon:

    It is there,
    There behind that blue veil

At the back of that mountain
It is there yonder
Where she lives—
His happiness, his life and all.

There in the land of his virulent enemy,
The enemy against which he had fought
    countless battles,
The enemy whose weapon had riddled his
    body with scars,

She rested supinely, peacefully, unpolluted;
Beckoning to him to go for her,

For it was for him that she was born.

And he would go.
Now he would go—
Go, cross the valleys, climb the hills,
Descend the slopes, defy the enemies

Until he reached her,
His happiness, his dream-come-true.

And while she was his love, his satisfaction,
She was his mother's sorrow
And his people's ruin.

His bows and arrows in hand
He shook with potent manhood
And shuddered with glowing love of youth.

And he left alone,
With love to encourage him.

And when he came back
With his love beside him
The sheep and the goats
That he brought along
Bleated his name,
And the bulls' bells
Sang his praises.

F. N. BARASA

The Dark Darkness

The trees, young and old,
Gathered together and whispered.

The wind, like a messenger,
Whistled to himself solitarily.

The darkness, blaming himself,
Yet knowing not what to do,
Bit his knuckles with worry.
And they watched and witnessed
A young virgin,
Whose purity they feared,
Die by hanging
For the love she dearly needed—
The love she was denied.

The trees and the wind,
Perturbed, restless, fidgeted
And persuaded themselves to sleep and to forget:
For it could not be helped.

The darkness,
Black as soot with confusion,
Alone as death,

Tried to murmur himself to sleep:
"Love is to blame—not me."
But sleep wouldn't come.

For the moon in her heavenly abode
Was cursing and crying:
"If the girl dies,
Darkness with your blackness
Must take the blame.
For your clammy lightlessness
Is the cause of all this."

And the darkness grew darker
With worry and self-condemnation,
And when the girl wriggled
Nobody saw her;
When she died
Nobody was there.

A Guinean, ANSOUMANI SOUMAH was born in Conakry in 1943. He received his Secondary education at Conakry Technical College and then studied in the Institute of Languages there, before coming to do a B.A. degree at the University College, Dar es Salaam. His three poems in this anthology show variety both of subject matter and of treatment: the nostalgic re-creation of infancy in *Black Woman* (similar to the opening of Lay's *L'Enfant Noir*); the more public theme of *Unity*; and, in his latest poem, *Rendez-Vous*, the attempt to express a lover's frustration at the slowness of time.

Black Woman

I still feel
The heat of your glossy back
On my belly
Oh! Black Woman.
I still hear
The throb of your heart
In my ear, on your scapula
Oh! Black Woman.
I still smell
Your sweat in the burning sun,
Under your arm-pit
Oh! Black Woman.
I still feel
The cool heat of my urine,
Running straight down your legs
Oh! Black Woman.
Twenty four years have passed
I still remember.

Unity

On the peak of her majesty
On her permanent ice
Among the clouds
Which pass to and fro
On the highest peak of Africa
Looms up a word
   Unity.

Unity, I shout your name
Kilimanjaro shouts your name.
The echo is frittered away.
Mount Kenya answers
   Unity.

The echo soars up
Fouta Jallon answers
   Unity.

People of Shaka
People hundred divided into hundred
Unity implores you
The echo looms up
From her majesty
And soars up
From the South
To the vast hot extent of North
East, West, Centre, North and South
People hundred divided into hundred
Come together again
And shout at once
   Unity.

Rendez-vous

Boom——boom——boom
Heart beat . . .
Shiverings of impatience
And the earth turns like a chameleon
The clock hands are stuck
And the convulsing wish
Speed the earth's rotation
All over the world
Bring the clock hands
To the wanted hour
Shiverings of impatience
And the sun disappears so slowly
And the convulsing wish
Regardless of the heat
Stand behind the red disc
And pull it down
Down——down——down
Boom——boom——boom
Heart beat
And time is so slow

Born in Kampala in 1944, AUSTIN BUKENYA went to a Secondary School there, before coming to study in Dar es Salaam. Scholarships took him to York and Tananarive and in 1968 he became the first student at Dar to receive a First-Class Honours Degree. He is now a Special Assistant in the English Department at Makerere, and is also working on a postgraduate degree. His play, *The Secret*, was included in a volume of *Short East African Plays*, published by Heinemann in 1968. His two poems here deal with a similar eme and indeed *Naturally* may be read as a sequel to *One Same World*. ın both poems Bukenya is writing with ironic restraint about the contrast between the educated, Westernised elite of East Africa and the uneducated labourers; underlying both is the threat of violence that may be generated from such a contrast, expressed most powerfully by the one-word, last line of the second poem.

One Same World

A scarlet Persian carpet caresses the floor,
And chairs imperially ranged in a half-moon
Behind a stunted table, whose coffee-flower white
Cloth, with all its embroideries dazzles
The balcony from wall to wall with the reflected
    sun—

The sun whose bite upraises juices which mingle
Upon the backs of the labourers below
With the dust their matchetts raise from
The stones.

The chatter upon the balcony rises—the dance,
    the films,
The novels, the football, the cars, the boys and girls,
The newest fashion from Rome—the top of the
    pops—

"Harambee!" below, as a stone faithfully and deeply
Cuts into the greasy hands that heave it aside.

"Noisy rogues!" above—the loungers angry at being
Interrupted by the cry of unified effort.

A waiter in blank, merciless white bends
Over the coffee on the dwarf balcony table—

Below, a desperate "Harambee!" dries upon the
    parched throats.

Naturally

I fear the workers: they writhe in bristling grass
And wormy mud: out with dawn, back with dusk;
Depart with seed, and return with fat-bursting fruit:
And I eat the fruit.

And still they toil: at boiling point,
in head-splitting noise and threatening saws:
They suck their energy from slimy cassava
And age-rusty water taps: till they make a Benz.

And I ride in the Benz: festooned with
Striped rags and python copper coiling monsters
While the workers clap their blistered hands,
And I overrun their kids.

They build their hives: often out
Of the broken bones of fallen mates:
And I drone in them—"state-house"
Them, "collegise" them, officialize them.

And I . . . . I whore their daughters
Raised in litter-rotting hovels
And desiring a quickquick highhigh lifelife
To break the bond.

And I tell the workers to unite:
Knowing well they can't see hear or understand:
What with sweat and grime sealing their ears
And eyes already blasted with welding sparks,
And me speaking a colourless tongue.

But one day a rainstorm shall flood
The litter-rotten hovels and
Wash the workers' ears and eyes clean,
Refresh the tattered muscles for a long-delayed
Blow.

W. D. KAMERA

WILLIAM KAMERA was born in Moshi in 1942 and was at school in the north of Tanzania until 1964. He completed his B.A. degree at Dar es Salaam in 1969. His poems have previously appeared in *Transition* and *Drum Beat* (E.A.P.H.) and in 1965 he won an award in an East African Literature Bureau competition. *The Suns of Home* tells of the pain of a boy leaving his mother.

The Suns of Home

When I first opened my petals, mother,
The world took shape after my fashion;
And as the rose,
I unfolded and loomed
When the sun was cool
The air fresh and fair.

We knew no fear
Then, we did not care,
Alas the waves of the years!
The roses are living on the rains of yore
With their petals outstretched in prayer
   (Or is it despair?)

Mother dear, I must rise and go:
I'm tossed between two Poles,
The Pole of Do and the Pole of Don't.
   So hard to go in disguise these days,
Thanks, mamma, for all these years.
Then let me rise and go before the tides close in.
I will go with the cool sunrise before the waters rise.

   Tell them I have gone with the moon,

Tell them I have gone. No more!
Tell them—
Naked as I was born
I leave my clothes, mother dear, for your
    remembrance.
I'll be changed and new when I come again.
I'll look gloomy, pale and insane:

Wonder not mother dear—
I won't lose the shirt you knit me when I was young.
    Alas I have gone with the moon,
To return a pale new child.
Tell them I climbed the walls fearlessly
To the sandy top:
Do not lose hope,
    Tell them I have seen the land of the moon.

PETER SONGA studied at the University College, Dar es Salaam, graduated in 1968, and is now teaching near Kampala. *The Return* is a fine evocation of the sights, sounds and smells of a moonlit village, and the traveller's guilt at having neglected his home for the "burnt sands" and "ghost-like cities" which have disappointed and disillusioned him: "poisonous honey." In contrast, *Glow Worms and Shooting Stars* is a more meditative and private poem.

The Return

Here the shadows fall deep and dark
By moonlight—the water, a dirty-white snake
Among the deep dark shadows.
The air is light—a slight rustle of drooping leaves.
The owl hoots, animals sigh, crickets call,
Voices murmur. A glowing red through their legs.
A thread of warm brown smoke lifts towards the
        moon;
Sometimes falling, enveloping them.
A choking cough, an upturned face; familiar.
Smoke-smell mingled with dung odours
Drift towards me, hiding there—

Where burnt sands yield sour fruits of labour;
Where ghost-like cities breathe and sigh and throb
And the spirit reposes on giddy housetops:
Since when I left with the wind of locusts
After the scourge—a devastating world
We left—to scan new worlds, promising honey.
Poisonous honey it was. Sweet delusion!
Now in my shame would cry:

"You knew me well you voices, odours
And shadows—O receive the culprit,
Hiding there—Stretch out and find out me!"

P. W. SONGA

Glow-worms and Shooting Stars

Each on-and-off glow
 threading the night sky;
The headlong plunge
 of a blazing tail, signify
Resolutions passed
 from birth to death.
The brief span,
 without contemplation,
A life achieved
 in jealous joy.

Sitting there, a-wonder,
You are the artist
 that should have been,
Had not some unwandering hand
Resolutely smeared and splotched
Where your itching mind
 had mirrored double images:
Glow-worms and shooting stars
 come and go; cheating you.

Nightly fireworks
 streak and gently flicker;
Stroke the black obsession.
Overwhelming impulses of night,
 fevering flesh like raging blood,
Float half-answered questions:
Glow-worms and shooting stars

resolve and dissolve;
Half-cheating you.

Concepts in the mind,
  flitting in blurred blankness,
Break into single birth
  of crystal brightness:
Glow-worms and shooting stars,
  resolute passing passions,
Deceive, half-deceive,
  and undeceive.

BARNABUS KATIGULA was born in Mwanza in 1944 and educated at Nyegezi and Tabora before coming to the University College, Dar es Salaam. His first novel will soon be published by the East African Literature Bureau. *To An Orphan* expresses the deserted father's love and pity for his motherless daughter; a mixture of emotions—love and hate—is also present in his second poem, *I Never Knew To Hate.*

To an orphan

Little child
Indulged in physical exercise
Of your patient gums
With midsized lumps of sugar of clay
In early germination
Before you wholly settle your vacant region
With a maize-like population,
You pass the lazy hours thus
Harming your innocent self
Meaning well

Your mother
Bored with life fled away
Across the clouds beckoning us to follow
But unable to obey.

Dear child I'm your father, Your Mother's equal
Though unable to suckle you.

Don't rebel now
To hurry your pace away to mama
Who rebelled against us
Because life was stubborn.

My heiress, you hold my destiny.

When you fill your little head with sense
You'll know that I'm your father and son.
But while I'm yet your father
Sit by me. Hand me that lump of clay.
Alas our milk's asleep; no sucking till sunset.
Let's shake this cold potato, and hurry your age.

Daughter dear,
You are learning life younger than I did.
While I pity I envy you. Ah
There you release a flash of smile
Not knowing why,
Or did you hear your mother's cough?
We are both orphans but I fail to smile.
Come rest on my lap and teach me to smile.

I never knew to hate

Never did I know to hate
Until I learnt to love
And first felt
The insecurity of love
And the threat of loss
When suddenly
As women are wont,
Such is their immense tact,
Mine turned half her cheek away
Without warning
And poured impotent venom in me.

HASTINGS OKOTH-OGENDO was born in Kisumu District in Kenya in 1944 and educated at Maseno and Alliance High Schools. He then came to the University College, Dar es Salaam, to study Law which, he finds, "can become such a routine sometimes." In addition to *The Dancing Maniac*, he has published work in the *East African Journal* and the *Denning Law Society Journal*. *The Dancing Maniac* is the love-song of a frustrated and angry lover, the success of whose love finally rekindles himself and also revivifies the rest of his village. The poem is a fine re-creation of the traditional relationship between two lovers and their society; and between the society of the living and the world of the dead ancestors.

The Dancing Maniac

I

Mine speaks in the language of violence
   It sings not in whispers
   behind closed doors,
   Nor spells the soft letters of frail embrace
   And the closeness of the lip suck-suck.
   Unknown to me are the wild tears
   they shed in dark corners
   and the soft music of the paint in their secret eyes.
   Untrodden are the dreamlands of civilised love:
   The nose-nosing of flower-power,
   The eternity of sand-bathing,
   The waves that mumble in soft tunes at their feet;
   The cafe-house,
   The sweltering passions in the dance halls
   And the charms of the sunset
   that heralds the nice big moon.

II

Mistress, hear me cry:
   I cry with the voice of an agonised male
   For my being gropes for a pathway
   That leads to my fulfilment
   But my wounded heart bleeds
   and my going is frustrated.
   This soul; this holy flesh of mine,
   This pain of growth:

The very symbol of my rebellion:
This is the language of a depraved man.
It is the sign of unfinished workmanship
It is an abyss, an utter abandonment—
It is the protest of a disappointed soul.

III

The village shall be my witness
For my mistress has killed my being
And protest fingers prick from within my frame.
The third day is past,
The fourth half gone;
Weep, sinless love, weep!
Mine is not for the third day:
But the resurrection of a life time.

IV

Shall I talk to the caves in the hillside
And let the oracle echo my message
to those restless armpits—
Or stir those naked breasts
breathing over your ochred belly?
I'll talk to the tattoos on your face,
To the small of your back
And the oil you smeared there
Will I speak.
Let my words subdue your round bottoms
Oh! let them compel those red beads from your hips
and the ornaments your grandmother gave you—
From the smoothness of your neck,
Let me compel them.
It is to your scarless thighs
That I plead my love.

V

Will you come with me, my mistress?
We'll go to the market-place
Amidst our sweating fishermen.
Come with me to the village ground
Or to the mountain top
Where all can see us.
We'll stand in the blazing sun,
In the scorching heat of the noonday sun;
In the plain, plain, plains of our neighbourhood
We shall stand.
Follow me to the fig-tree
To the seat of my ancestors;
And there will I demonstrate the anger of my love;
With all my people there
Their heartbeats throbbing consent
I will let loose this caged spirit upon you.
Then I will be satisfied,
Whole,
Finished,
A being again.
It shall be my resurrection—
Come!
For the drums of my calling
are tight with greeting!

VI

My mistress came to the village ground;
She was a dancing maniac;
The blessed virgin of the ancestors
Dancing to the tune of the tom-toms
Casting an evil spell over the yellow evening sky.
The village watched her fall into a trance

And were caught in a frenzy too;
The youth dance was whole;
'Twas sacred witchcraft
Unearthing the forgotten days of mystic fertility
And the potency of her womanhood.
As she swayed her chocolate hips
Her spear-pointed breasts
Twitching with welcome
I touched the noose of my goatskin
And felt the music there.
My crude garments crumbled at my feet
And I stood before her,
Naked with truth.

VII

She heaved a sigh;
   And as I watched her dancing away
   Malicious and wicked like an offended ancestor god
   I, too, fell into a trance.
   My loins bubbled with the desire of a
      malignant male
   With violence unto death,
   I wept after her.

VIII

At last I had found my maker
   And to the shrine of my ancestors
   I followed her.
   That feeling of eternal restlessness,
   That perpetual darkness, was spent
   And the dawn of my new life was beginning to glow.

IX

As my maker charmed the sacred tree
   I rose as from a drunken stupor
   And saw lying at my feet,
   The remains of my former self.
   The carcase of that which once I was
   lay decomposing at my feet
   and as the fumigation rose to meet the sky
   I was glad.
   Yes,
   I was very glad
   As I saw my contorted past wither
   And the remains sink and disappear
   The ugly scars—
   The signs of my painful victory
   Spread like a dung heap at my maker's feet
   And I tell you yet again
   I was glad as I peeled off those sapless scales.

X

The village was glad to witness the profane
   resurrection
   The beginning of an endless life for their son;
   And their tired nerves quivered with life again.
   I saw the gladness shining in their round faces
   It was there in the flatness of their noses
   and the hollow of their cheeks
   It was in their merry laughter;
   Their blessing flowed in tears of joy
   And in the flood
   I floated to the height of completeness.

XI

Even our children joined the festival
   Naked from their pot holes
   They watched with dirt-ringed faces
   and screamed aloud with joy.
   They, too, saw the garbage heap
   that was my former self
And they were glad.

XII

The shrill voices of our women
   As they sang to the fullness of virginity
   And the passions of manhood
   Filled the twilight air;
   Augmenting the feverish rhythm
   Of the crazen drummers.
   And as I stood naked before her
   Pulsing to the heat of manhood
   My blood rushed with vigour
   to steady my tender spine.
   Now I would be free
   Alive again.
   It was the beginning of a new growth.

XIII

As the drums rose to a frenzy
My hand—my new hand, went out
   And touched the blessed virgin.
   She was offended no more
   as I danced into the arena with her;
   To the gentle tune of my ancestors

and the rich smell of the refuse of their issues—
The welcome scent of the cattle lingering in the air
I danced with the maniac my maker.

XIV

Then the sun went down to rest—
  The fire glows—
  The sacrifice is over.
The wind blows:
Spirits,
Heartbeat.
Silence;
And I was alone no more.

Part II
PROSE

MIRIAM NJERU was born in Nyeri, Kenya, in 1944 and completed her B.A. degree at Dar es Salaam in 1969. The brief *Excusable Anarchist* tells of a young Kikuyu girl's innocent involvement with Mau Mau and her bewilderment, soon to develop into hatred, at finding her parents dead and her home razed to the ground. *Smoke and Dust*, set in the present, also deals with a conflict: between an educated girl, living in the town, and her uneducated mother-in-law, with the husband and son, Ndung'u, caught between these two cross-fires. *Smoke and Dust* charts the pain and dislocation experienced by a society in transition.

The excusable anarchist

Muthoni was a young, growing girl, full of the innocence of youth.

As she worked in the garden with her mother, or played at home with her brother and the other boys, she would hear rumours of a gang of people living in the forest. They were terrible people, wicked and cruel, as she could gather from the women's conversation. But her brother and the other boys gave her the impression that this gang was the ideal for any young man alive. Her brother often wished that he could be allowed to join this gang. She knew for certain that these forest dwellers were the Mau Mau.

But before she had learnt anything more about them, her brother suddenly disappeared from home, never to return. She did not know where he had gone, and she could not venture to ask. Her home became a night meeting-place shortly afterwards; men, thickly clad in military coats, looking like policemen, came and talked in low, deep voices for hours on end. She never discovered what the meetings were intended for. Before long, her father was sending her on errands to tell various people that they were wanted. She would be advised to go cautiously and attract as little notice as possible.

One quiet evening, her mother gave her a basket full of maize, beans, bananas, potatoes and all sorts of vegetables. She was to take this food to the forest, to a particular spot, and give it to the men who would be awaiting her there. Muthoni made her way into the quiet, desolate forest. Long tree shadows, dotted by beams of moonlight, surrounded her. She was afraid of the night, and of the shadows; but she preferred walking under the shadows, where she would be less likely to attract attention, to the open, clear patches.

She knew the way well, however, and before long she was with General Chege's men. She found them feasting on a bull, probably stolen, and there was a lot of gaiety in the forest. The men welcomed her cordially, especially because of the food she had brought. They were also happy because they had found a cook in this girl. Muthoni prayed to them on her knees to let her go home, but in vain. A month went by before she knew where she was.

In the meantime, her parents had got into trouble with the police, because of Muthoni's absence. They had at first succeeded in convincing the police that Muthoni was visiting an aunt for two or three days, and they had been told to send for her. A week passed, two weeks, three .... and finally a month, and still there was no sign of Muthoni. There was no news either.

After a month, Muthoni managed to get a day's leave to go and see her parents. She went the way she had come, but this time with a much lighter heart, expecting to find her parents waiting to receive her. She was so thrilled that she hardly noticed anything on her way. It was, therefore, not until she was on the site of her home that she noticed anything wrong.

Black ashes covered the ground, livestock carcasses lay about, rotting and filling the air with an abominable stench. She panicked. She looked for her home, but what could she see where it had stood but a black heap? She sat down and wept gall for the home she had lost. She wondered what had caused this hellish destruction.

Where would she go? Where were her parents, anyway? Who had done this? Where were all the neighbours? All these questions raced through her mind, but the answers to them did not. "Well", she said to herself, "I will try the market-place. If there's no one there . . . then I don't know what to do." She set off in the direction of the market-place. Whether she walked, ran, or flew, she could not tell; she only found herself there.

She looked round. She saw people, dead, dying, and living. She wondered what made the living keep company with the dead. Surely people are buried when they die? Her grandfather anyway had been buried. And what about those who were moaning, writhing and groaning? They should have gone to hospital, but why hadn't they? Even if she could find answers, none would have been satisfactory. For she noticed that the whole village was gathered here in the market-place. People were huddled together in the shops, on verandahs and in latrines.

It was a miserable sight. She listened to the people talking, and at last realised that the *Home Guards* had set the homes on fire and had sent these people here because they were believed to be on good terms with the Mau Mau.

Muthoni could not find her parents anywhere. She at last joined her aunt's family. She asked questions but nobody was willing to answer her. Instead of information she received blank gazes, sympathetic and affectionate at best, but not communicating anything definite, except fear.

After a week of a racking suspense, and after many short, discreet questions, she learnt that her parents were dead. Like many other villagers, they had been burnt to death in their house. Muthoni was too horrified, too hardened by the beastly conditions surrounding her, to shed a tear. She sat in tearless grief, and a sudden hardness of heart and stubbornness filled her. She hated the *Home Guards* with all her powers. She longed for an opportunity when she would get her own back, when she would revenge her parents' cruel death.

Muthoni grew up with her aunt in the village, never free to do anything she would have liked to do, and with a deep hatred for anyone working for, or with the Government; Government for her was a symbol of cruelty.

Smoke and dust

Her mother-in-law's previous visit had ended in chaos and scandal. The scandal had spread over every village like a swarm of locusts, destroying Ruth's name and that of all "educated" women. It was said that when Nyokabi, her mother-in-law, arrived, she had been halted at the gate.

"Kamau", Ruth and shouted. "Bring the D.D.T. pump. She must be sprayed!" Obedient Kamau had brought the pump, thinking "Had it been *my* wife...". Ruth had gone to the gate and started pumping at the astonished Nyokabi.

"What's the matter?", Nyokabi had asked.

"You see, I am sure you have fleas and lice and if I allow you to come in like that you will infect the whole house."

Nyokabi wondered, "Is this Ruth?" As a rule she was very clean—head always clean-shaven and her blue sheet always washed and stored for visits like this. This was her "Sunday-best" and there was no possibility of lice. Her everyday sheet, red-dyed, was always put in the sun the minute she scratched herself, hoping to get rid of any offender—fleas mostly. True she was old but nevertheless the younger generation could hardly match her cleanliness, both in body and in the home. Ruth's claim overcame her with astonished submissiveness and she felt Ruth might be justified in her action.

In the house, she was taken straight to the bathroom, to wash her feet in Dettol-filled water—in case of jiggers. Not that she was infected, but just to make sure. Nyokabi was even more astonished. She tried to think of Ruth as she had known her. Before her son Ndung'u married her, he had brought her home two or three times. She, indeed everyone, had been impressed by the quiet girl from Murang'a. They had never talked, except in the exchange of the customary greetings, and Nyokabi had felt the girl was shy and not very talkative. She had been glad to encourage her son to marry Ruth, an educated girl and a Primary School teacher.

After this great ordeal, Nyokabi was taken to the kitchen where she was handed a mug of warm porridge and was astonished to hear Ruth say, "Are you staying for lunch?" Nyokabi would have screamed if she had not been so astonished. "Is this an African custom?", she wondered.

"I am not hungry", was all she could say.

"In that case, you had better go and wait outside while Kamau prepares our lunch. You can take that stool and sit in the shade." Ruth said this indifferently, as if to a child who was being a nuisance.

As soon as Ndung'u had come from work, Nyokabi had explained that she had not come to stay and insisted on catching a bus that very afternoon. Ndung'u tried to persuade her to change her mind and stay for several days. He appealed to Ruth to support him in the invitation but all she could say was: "I have some guests tonight, remember dear". And in English too. So Ndung'u had been obliged to see his mother to the bus stop. He tried to ask her why she had changed her mind so soon but all he got was—"I just wanted to see you children. I am very glad I came and found you all well. Goodbye!", she said, as she entered the bus for her home.

"When will you come back?", Ndung'u asked, but the bus had already started and he was obliged to wave back her farewell.

That had been about two years ago. Ndung'u had been ignorant of the whole incident. True it had spread far and wide but only amongst the "low" circles—not in Ndung'u's circle. And anyway, if he had heard it, don't some people decide to tear apart and kill characters? People were malicious, weren't they, and could decide to ruin his relationship with gentle Ruth. He had definitely suspected something wrong between his wife and his mother, but never anything so serious. His wife could never be induced to visit his home and he attributed it to other things.

"To do what, darling?", she would ask when the husband suggested a ride home. "Surely we have nothing to do there, and remember all that dust and all that smoke! You cannot drink any water there without getting a cold. It tastes of smoke and dust. And then all those people coming to greet you and all the time hoping you will give them at least a shilling each! Darling, let's go to Nakuru this weekend, or to Mombasa. Surely we can afford a hotel. Or you know what, darling? You have been promising to take me to 'Treetops'. We can stay the night at the Outspan Hotel, or—oh, I have it! You know Jane! Her husband is teaching at Nyeri and they could put us up for the night. I'll ring her."

"But surely, Ruth", Ndung'u would try to argue, "You know very well those people at home just love having us around and making us their idols. They are all my relatives and not as dirty as you imagine. After all, I grew up with them!"

Not that Ruth herself was very clean. She was lazy, preferring her bed to the kitchen. She would never have managed that home had it not been for the two man-servants, and rumour had it that had it not been for their great need of money—with famine and children at home—the two men would have quit ages ago.

At last Ruth had her long-awaited son—her first-born. Ndung'u was very proud of her and slaughtered a goat to congratulate her. Weeks went by and with each week Ruth grew lazier and lazier. All she did was occupy herself with breast-feeding and napkin-changing. The soiled napkins would be thrown into the bath, in the hope that one of the servants would wash them. And woe to the man who decided he couldn't!

Three weeks after the baby's birth, Ndung'u came

from work very excited. He had received a letter from home, congratulating him. The letter said that his mother was coming to see her "young husband", as the child was named after Ndung'u's father.

Ruth feared the letter.

"Now she just wants to bring those bananas again. I wonder whether they grow anything else there in the reserves apart from those starchy foods—bananas, maize, potatoes, arrow-roots. They seem to think we rejoice in such kinds of foods, like beggars content with whatever is given them. How can one survive it all—such an unbalanced diet and so dirty, to crown it all."

"One would think you had been brought up in State House, Ruth, instead of in that rounded hut from which I rescued you," Ndung'u had said, too calmly.

"I wish I had been! And you know very well you didn't rescue me! You know very well that you are very lucky you found me and got me. Do you realise how many men wanted me and how many I turned down, all for you?" She was shouting now; Ndung'u was trying to calm her.

"Yes, I realise", said Ndung'u. "I realise how many you turned down because they had no cars; how many you turned down because they didn't have responsible and well-paid jobs; and how many because they didn't have good houses and they couldn't afford them. I realise only too well, Ruth, how you accepted me quickly so as not to miss my "404", this good house in Karen and of course my several thousand shillings a year. Ruth, don't think I'm a kid. I may have been quiet for a long time but don't attribute that to weakness. I want us to be happy, forget why we chose one another, find new values in each other and love one another for our own sakes. I know you did not love me as much as I loved you when we were married. You wanted to escape the country and live in the city but let's forget that. With our children, we shall support one another. And now"—his calmness had deserted him—"And now,

42

you have to treat my mother like a human being. Without her and her 'dirt', you would not have found me. You have to accept her. It is not her fault that you lost your mother, Ruth. She could be your mother too, and you know she loved you very much before we got married."

"Then let her not bring her dirty foodstuffs here", screamed Ruth. "Tell her that if I want maize or bananas, I prefer to buy them myself in the market. And sometimes your jewel of a mother has the impudence to bring cooked food! I don't want to catch typhoid. Who knows how she cooked it, what kind of water she used and the utensils! She cooks on a wood fire with all that smoke getting into the food and it tastes of nothing but smoke!"

"Then you can teach her to cook with gas or electricity", Ndung'u said bitingly. "You forget she hasn't had a formal education like you and no instruction in cookery or what you call Domestic Science. What she knows was handed down to her by her mother. Perhaps you could teach her how to cook *irio* in a better way. Or better still, how to bake, provided, of course, you provide her with an oven and everything else she will need. Had my mother gone to school, she would have got a very excellent grade. She is very quick to learn."

His calmness and sarcasm infuriated her. "Okay", she said. "Let your precious mother come, but she should not think she is going to soil my bed or sheets. Luckily, there are plenty of sacks in the house and one old ironing blanket. The sooner she comes and goes, the better for us all!"

"I warn you not to do anything rash, Ruth, because you might just regret it", Ndung'u said on his way out.

That night he stayed out until very late, but she did not miss him. She was too busy sulking to really think seriously of him. When he came back, she was already fast asleep. She did not speak to him the following morning although he shouted "Okay baby. See you at lunch and my old woman will be pleased to see the baby."

She had already decided on her course of action but

it was no use telling him. He just refused to see things her way, deliberately refusing to see her way of thinking. And it had been like that, she mused, ever since they got married. He had insisted on her not working. "After all dear, you should rest at home and make us a home", he has argued. "You won't miss much as my salary can cover it ten times over." He was working with the City Council and he was very well paid. "Very soon", he had said, "I'll be on the top scale and I don't want my wife to kill herself with overwork. I'll let electricity do it", he had joked. She remembered now that she had thought him an angel for such a proposition. She had guessed the idle hours she had to kill. She had tried visits to various friends; she had chatted and gossiped until she was dry. She had learnt that most of her friends did not welcome their mothers-in-law. They considered them a nuisance. "You are just foolish, my dear", they had told her, "for allowing your husband to go home so often. She will soon influence him against you. They are all alike, these old women."

She remembered that Ndung'u was attached to his mother indeed. Why wasn't he hers wholly?

While all these thoughts raced across her mind, she dozed off and the cry of the baby woke her up at ten o'clock. She bathed and fed the baby. "Kamau", she called into the kitchen, "Add an extra meal for lunch. That woman is coming."

Kamau did not have to be told who "that woman" was. He was very familiar with Ruth's dislike for "that woman" and he had not been deaf yesterday during that great quarrel.

Ruth had hardly settled the baby in the pram when she heard Ndung'u's honking and saw, through the bedroom window, Ndung'u helping his mother out of the car. She did not stir. What was there to hurry for and the woman would be here for . . . . She continued watching the many baskets which were emerging from the back of the car. She saw Kamau rush out to help take

44

them into the kitchen. "I wish he would take them to his home", Ruth thought.

"Mother, come in", she heard Ndung'u shouting. "Just like a boy", Ruth thought.

"Ruth must be feeding the baby and so you will have to excuse her", he lied, knowing very well that the baby was usually asleep at that time. "Come in and sit down, mother."

"Is there anywhere I can wipe my feet?", she asked quietly. "Don't bother, mother. These houses do not clean themselves and after all what are floors for? To be made dirty so that they can be washed. What's the use of having something you're afraid of dirtying? You become a slave. Whether dirty or not, this house has to be cleaned daily, so you should provide us with some work. Ruth is very good at housekeeping."

Nyokabi laughed and entered the house. Ndung'u made her comfortable on one of the sofas.

"How do you manage to live in such a house?", she asked. "There is no room for movement. Everywhere you turn, chairs, tables and books. And what is that thing there with the pale face?"

"That is called television. In that you can see what people are doing. When they are reading the news, you can see the person reading it and you hear him."

"Aiya, aiya!", she exclaimed. "The whiteman will give us wonders. They began by giving people goats' teeth. They can go through the sky. Kanuki was telling me that they have given a man a heart from a dead body and the man is alive. Aiya! I don't think there is anything left for the whiteman to do now. My son, the whiteman is the greatest wizard, stronger than any of our strongest magicians. Wonderful things will always happen to make us hold this great magician in awe."

Ndung'u laughed at this. "But they are like anyone else, mother. It is just that they are richer."

"Agreed. Show me a black man who can perform such a great magical act", she said.

45

Before Ndung'u could answer, Ruth passed on her way to the kitchen.

"Hi, Ruth! Mother is here!"

"I know", said Ruth. "How do you do?", she said, ignoring the outstretched hand of the mother. "Excuse me, I must go into the kitchen."

"How is my young husband?", asked Nyokabi.

"He is sleeping."

"Can I see him?" For answer, Ruth ran back into the bedroom and came out pushing a pram, covered with a mosquito-net. "There! You can see him!"

Nyokabi bent down to admire the baby. She touched the net and was going to lift it aside to admire the baby better when Ruth intervened.

"Don't touch the net or remove it. See him through it and finish quickly. His sleep is being disturbed."

Nyokabi, without thinking, did what she intended to do.

"Tut, tut"—she was spitting very tiny particles of saliva on the net, to bless the child—her "husband."

Ruth almost toppled over. She snatched the net, rushed the pram into the bedroom and ran into the bathroom to soak the net.

All this while, Ndung'u had been standing speechless, not believing his eyes or ears. So Ruth's threats had been sincere! He went into the bedroom and didn't know what to think or how to act. He had never experienced such a thing before. On impulse, he took the child from the pram and went with it to the sitting-room.

"Mother, here is your husband!", he said, trying to be light. He tried to hand the baby to Nyokabi, but she hesitated and wondered whether she should take it. But Ndung'u looked so sincere in his offer, so innocent and wounded, that she touched the baby. Ndung'u sat down next to her and pushed the baby into her yet-undecided hands. "Take it, mother. At least hold him once and give him your blessing. He will have a hard upbringing."

Then she took the baby and hugged it. The baby woke

46

up with a yell. Ruth heard the yell and rushed from the bathroom. She stood momentarily spell-bound at seeing the child in Nyokabi's hands.

"What are you doing with him?", she asked after recovering. "Don't you realise he doesn't like you, else he wouldn't have cried? Ndung'u, why did you have to wake him up? Surely your mother could have waited until he woke up?" She snatched the baby. "He doesn't like old people, somehow", she added, realising that she had been too hard on Nyokabi. "Now I have to give him another bath otherwise he will smell the whole day long. And the Mbuguas are coming to tea."

"To hell with the Mbuguas. I'll put them off", said Ndung'u. Then he controlled himself. His mother was present he remembered. Ruth took the baby back to the pram and Ndung'u followed her.

"You have to control yourself, dear—your tongue and your actions leave soot and mud on us. If we have to live together, you have to behave", he whispered.

"Now what have I done wrong? You want the baby to get sick, coming into contact with . . ."

"Be quiet", he interrupted, hissing in anger. "Be quiet or else . . . ." He slapped her hard and left her to weep in silence. He found the table already set. He invited his mother to come to the table. She insisted on eating where she was but he persisted. In the end she gave in and went to the table.

"Isn't Ruth eating?", she asked. He knew very well that after what had happened she would refuse to eat.

"Forget about her. She says she is not hungry."

During the meal they did not mention Ruth any more. Nyokabi told him all the news about home and their problems.

"Is it possible for me to go home tonight?", she asked as they left the table.

"You must stay longer, mother. It's a long time since I saw you and there is so much we haven't talked about." Mother and son were always close.

"Okay, I stay until tomorrow. But tomorrow I must go home. You see, I couldn't get anybody to leave my goats with. There are only children at home and I am sure I will find the goats starved to death and the house burnt down."

Ndung'u took his mother outside under the shade and they both sat there, comfortably enjoying and relishing one another's company. For them, the afternoon was too short. Ruth did not appear once. She kept to her room and her baby.

By evening, Ruth had got over her shock and when Ndung'u and his mother were having supper, she went to prepare Nyokabi a bed. She stored away the bed and the mattress in the guest-room and made a very beautiful bed on the floor—with a mat, three sacks and two blankets. "That's actually a luxury bed for such a woman", thought Ruth who resented Nyokabi and blamed her for what had happened. She forgot that Ndung'u had told her he had brought Nyokabi a vono-bed and a mattress to go with it. After the meal, Ruth went to call Nyokabi to show her her room. Nyokabi went to collect her *kabuti* from the kitchen and Ndung'u went to see his mother's bed.

"She is not going to sleep on the floor", Ndung'u said quietly. "Bring that bed and mattress which is usually here. If need be, she will use my mattress but I am not having her sleep on a cold floor."

"But it's not cold. There's a mat under the three sacks and a blanket on top. The other blanket is for covering herself and don't forget she has a *kabuti*." The mother entered at this point and she knew that she had to act now and decide.

"Go to sleep, my children", she said. "I will be very comfortable here."

"But, mother . . . ." This was Ndung'u.

"Sh! Since when have you been running a home, Ndung'u? A home is a woman's right and domain. I'm comfortable. Go to sleep." And with that she closed the door behind the quiet couple. She lay awake long, wondering. The voices from the other room could be heard clearly—both raised in anger. She could hear Ndung'u now, telling his wife to pack and go if she could not behave decently, even to his own mother. There he was again, telling her she was responsible for Nyokabi deciding to leave tomorrow. There was Ruth defending herself, claiming that Ndung'u was only a big boy, still stuck to his mother like gum.

She tried not to listen but whoever can refuse the ear its food? Then things started moving around in the next room. Things fell and broke, and there was much movement. She heard the baby yelling above the tumultuous noise. Should she go for the baby, she wondered. She decided not. Then she heard it. A big, loud slap and the loud cry of a woman in pain. It pierced right through the house.

Nyokabi covered her head. The temptation to interfere was very great but she had to overcome it.

She lay awake, long after the crying of both the mother and the baby had ceased and all was quiet in the house. She could not sleep.

"What's wrong with the new generation?", she wondered. "The men are the women, or rather the wives, to be bossed by their husbands—the women. This is education and whiteman's power. Tomorrow I must go home where I belong. I should not think of coming back here." "Only death will ever bring me back here!", she vowed to herself, at dead of night. "After all, we are not of the same world."

IZZAT LALANI was born in Uganda in 1946 and completed her B.A. degree in Linguistics and Sociology in 1969. Her short story, *The Castle and the Ruins*, takes for its theme the relationship between a father and his crippled daughter whom he believes to possess supernatural powers.

The castle and the ruins

The branches elongated and coiled around him, tying him tightly to the tree trunk. Stunned, he did not even struggle to free himself. All those gigantic trees had life in them and they were dancing all over the place. He heard a giggle and gulped at the sight of Nakitto. She was standing just a few feet away from him with a huge green snake wound around her neck while a couple of others were in her hands. Fright seized his neck as Nakitto started laughing loudly. She walked back and forth, bringing the snakes right near his face. Oh, she was not limping—her polio was gone! What a big built woman she looked, instead of the crippled, seven year old child. As he saw Nakitto release one snake after another, he felt himself being enclosed in a blanket of ice that pricked his skin. Desperation hung in the air as Musoke screamed in a shaking voice, "Nakitto, what are you doing? I am your father, Nakitto. Stop it, I beg you..... Please..... Take them away....." But Nakitto did not hear him. She was waving her hands feverishly in the air and laughed deafeningly.

"Nakitto! You are a witch. I knew it all along. Wow!...." Something bit him and Musoke cried out in terror that went piercing through the sky.

Wet with perspiration, Musoke sat up in bed. A hand touched his shoulder. Petrified, he turned around and saw his wife Luandeka standing next to his bed. She said, in a gentle soothing voice, "What's the matter? Did you have a bad dream?"

He nodded. Then, taking a deep breath and at the same time wiping his forehead, said, "Oh! I am fine. You go back to sleep. I think I shall go out, since it is already dawn."

Luandeka opened her mouth to say something but changed her mind, seeing that puzzled expression on his face that had become too frequent an expression of his.

Outside, the early morning air was fresheningly chilly. Beyond the horizon a faint reddish-yellow patch could be seen, announcing the arrival of the daybreak that the chirruping birds were already welcoming. A little more than five feet tall, with drooping shoulders and hands hanging loosely at his sides, Musoke stood surveying the world around him. Finally he looked up at the sky and muttered, "It's going to be a hot day again." The long drought had destroyed most of the crops. If it continued a little longer, the whole village was going to be struck by famine. Bad luck had been born with Nakitto and the whole village knew it. Soon after her birth, there had been a series of heavy thunderstorms that had harmed the cotton crops. Then had come the spread of disease among the banana plantations, followed by the lowering of prices of coffee on the world market. And now this long drought! One problem after another had left a print on Musoke's face, making him look much older than his late thirties.

The death of Nalumasi had snatched away the youthful gaiety from his life. Since the day he had met her at his uncle's village, she had been his whole life. Everything about her was small and innocent—small, round eyes, a little thick nose and then lips slightly drooping at the sides. How hard he had worked to pay the huge bride-price demanded by her father. He was helped a little, though grudgingly, by his relatives, who claimed that he was bewitched by Nalumasi. It hurt him when people called her a witch even after her death. How could a person like Nalumasi be a witch? She was so naive and, after all, she had been just eighteen when he had married her. Musoke knew, like the others in the village, that she was not a good housewife: the meals were hardly ever ready on time, and the piles of banana-peels lay behind the house for days. But she loved him dearly and that is what mattered to him. The news that she had used some magic to keep Musoke subordinate to her had moved like a snowball during their married life. It was because he paid so much attention to her, unlike any man in her tribe; he hardly scolded her for being lazy and he never beat her, though she made mistakes.

Fate kicked him in the back the day Nakitto was born. It had never struck him that Nalumasi would ever leave him for good. Just a few minutes before she had closed her eyes for ever, she had whispered, while holding his hand, "Call her Nakitto. It is me, remember me . . . ." Her eyes had held a strange, pleading look—they seemed to say "I do not want to die. Do something . . . ." But he refused to believe that she was leaving him. For days to come, he was haunted by that strange pleading look that made him feel guilty that he could not give her the one thing that she had wanted so much. There were so many things about her that he remembered vividly even now—like her lazy yawn every morning and the way she carried a bunch of bananas on her head, pretending to be panting at the sight of him. Of late, he had been thinking about her a great deal more. Perhaps Nakitto was growing up to be so much like her mother. He would never forgive Nakitto for having snatched Nalumasi from him. It was because of Nakitto that he had married Nalumasi's younger sister Luandeka. There were hardly any striking resemblances between the two sisters though both of them gave Musoke what he was looking for in them—the first gave him love, the second a home. Though Nakitto was quite a burden in the house, Luandeka always took great care of her—perhaps because she felt sorry to see her husband hate Nakitto so much,

and the rest of the village accusing her for the occurrence of a number of mishaps in the village.

Musoke was awakened from his thoughts by his wife's voice saying "Aren't you going to do any work today?" After a short silence, she added in a little too casual a voice, "I am sorry about what I said yesterday. I was merely very upset," and she went back into the house.

Not bothering to answer, he started walking towards the cattle-shed. She had said that merely to make him feel much better, for her voice had given her away. The previous day's incident worked itself back into his mind. Around midday, when he was returning from the field, he saw his four year old son, Musa, playing in the compound with Nakitto.

He had some sort of feeling of uneasiness and so, before going into the house, he shot a quick glance at both children playing on the ground. He stopped and stared. There was something moving on the ground towards Musa. Before he could reach them, Musa had already been bitten by the snake. Frightened, Nakitto was sobbing loudly. Musoke managed to kill the snake, but Musa was already curling up in pain. While the weeping Luandeka ran for help, Musoke busied himself in saving his son's life, in which he succeeded. By evening nearly the whole village had come to see Musa, who was now running a high temperature. Word was spread that Nakitto was a witch and she had done this on purpose. The seed germinated by night in Luandeka's mind. Weeping bitterly, she told her husband, "Nakitto killed Nalumasi, and now she has tried to kill Musa. Don't you see what she is? Get rid of her, please, . . . get rid of her . . . . "

The words had worked on his mind the whole night and even now, as he watched his two cows, the words rang distinctly in the air. Perhaps people were right. She was a witch. Oh no! What a thought! It took Musoke a few minutes to realise that his wife was shouting for him to come quickly. He tried to run but he felt aged and feeble. He knew what had happened, looking at Luandeka beating her chest vigorously and weeping, "My Musa . . . Oh . . . ." There was a choking lump in his throat and his strength seemed to be sapping. He gripped a chair lying around, and suddenly noticed Nakitto standing in the doorway, her mouth half open, her cheeks stained with tears, her hands holding the crutches tightly.

Musoke's mouth closed in a vice-like grip, his hands curled into a fist, making the veins visible. Seeing through a smoky screen of anger and hatred, he pounced on Nakitto, throwing her off balance and onto the ground. Nakitto's frightful piercing screams were drowned in the loud thundering voice of Musoke, "Witch! You killed them both! Now I suppose it's going to be my turn. Devil . . ." He was hitting her as he used to hit the bugs in his house. Suddenly he became still, one of his hands hung half-way in the air, the other gradually released Nakitto's shoulder and he stared at the almost unconscious figure of his daughter on the ground. Then he whispered, "Nalumasi . . . Oh darling . . . Nalumasi," and he started stroking Nakitto's face gently. Yes, he had seen the same look in her eyes as Nalumasi had had just before she died—that helpless, pleading look. He held her close in his arms and carried her inside the house. This time he was going to make sure that she did not leave him.

That night, two shadows were seen walking slowly away from a house in the midst of the wailing crickets—a man carrying a young girl in his arms, and a woman with a bundle of clothes on her head and a few other things in her hands. No sooner had their figures become invisible than a brilliant red light stood out, defying the darkness and making apparent the figures of a group of men dancing and singing around the house. Shouts of "Witch! Kill her . . . Kill them all . . . Ooo . . . Oh . . . ." were heard. The smoke danced its way upwards to the sky as the house was gradually burned down to ashes, burying with it Musoke's past—the past with its magnificent castles that had made the present look like an ugly pile of ruins.

LYDIA KIMARO comes from Kenya and graduated from the University
College, Dar es Salaam in 1969. *The Fall of the Goat's Kingdom* is a modern
political allegory, told in the form of a traditional folk tale. It is of particular
interest as it is the only story in this collection that does not aim at a realistic
description of people and events.

The Fall of the Goat's Kingdom

Telling stories was our only entertainment. We always
gathered together round our elder sister and waited for
her to tell us stories. There were two of us who were
very young, and we hated each other like a woman and
a snake. Saki always tried to show that I knew nothing.
If there were no stories it meant going to bed early.
Our days were not like our parents' days. They could
go and dance in the moonlight, but those were the old
days of the savages, so they tell us. Missionaries have
taught us better: stay at home and keep yourself to
yourself; only monkeys go about making a noise at night.
One evening my elder sister told us a story. I really
liked it, although it made me weep. She started her story:
"A long time ago, before men started keeping goats,
all the goats lived in the forest, like other wild animals.
At that time goats were very funny; they lived in groups—
white goats, brown goats and black goats. They were
not enemies, but each kept to its own group. The white
goats lived in a valley, the brown goats lived on the slopes
of the mountains, and the black goats lived on top of the
mountain. There were lots and lots of goats, but they had
their enemy too—the lion. The lions in that region were
not as many, or even half as many as the goats, but
still the goats feared the lions." Here she paused. "Senga",
she called me—they all liked shortening my name as
if it was too much for their mouths to pronounce it all.

59

"Can you tell me why the goats feared the lions?",
she asked me. I would have told her had it not been for
the sharp look from Saki. I knew he was jealous because
I was asked. That sharp look made me unable to utter
a word; my mouth was left open and I was merely
dismissed to bed because my elder sister thought I was
yawning. "Well", my sister continued, "the goats feared
the lions because they could not eat the lions, nor harm
them in any way."

"So one day the chief of the black goats took his horn
and called his people. Then a message was sent round to
the other goats' kingdoms, and they were all asked to
meet on the mountain where the black goats lived. This
was the first meeting of all the goats and it was held
during the daytime when the lions were asleep. The
meeting was opened by the king of the black goats.
(We shall call him 'the black king' for convenience's sake.)
The black king delivered his speech: "Black brothers
and sisters, brown brothers and sisters, and white brothers
and sisters, it is a great pleasure to see you all here.
We have been living separately, but actually we belong
to one ancestor. We speak the same language, we eat the
same food, we carry our young ones in our womb for
the same number of days—in short, we are really one.
Now, my whole purpose for calling you here is not to
tell you that we are brothers and sisters, but to tell you
that, being so, why don't we unite.... Unity, my
brothers, is the thing", and he shouted again, jumping
up, "Unity, and let us attack our enemy. Our fathers
said that one tiger cannot kill a louse. So when we are
together, we shall be able to fight this monster." They all
shouted a chorus of approval, "Yes, it is time, it is time
we attacked the lion, yes it is time he was punished."
There was one old white goat sitting by himself. He did
not show any enthusiasm and when the chorus was over,
he cleared his voice and asked them, "How are you going
to attack them?" And the black king continued with
his speech.

"Yes, white brother, how are we going to attack the lion? That is the question. We have no claws, and our horns are so small that some of you I can see have none." They looked around at each other and burst out into a laugh. "That is not all", went on the black king, "we cannot bear the smell of blood or intestines: how then can we fight them? Well, the only solution is a cold war. We must sign a peace treaty with the lions. You may wonder, but I have figured all this out. We shall give the lion three helpless brothers from each colour, and we shall tell him that this is a sacrifice to him and we ask him to keep away from us, and feed on zebras, buck and the like. In return we shall worship him and give him meat only during the dry season when all the others who are not of our nation are dead. You agree, we shall see the lion today; if not, then you go back to the previous life."

They all agreed and on the same day the three kings, with their sacrifices, went to visit the lion. The lion was very happy, and promised not to kill them at all: but he gave them one condition—that they must keep together and not wander about on the mountains. The three kings were very pleased and promised the lion that they were going to keep in the valley, so that the bucks and the other animals could come and live in the place where they had moved away from. When they were going back to their homes, the white king was not very happy, but he did not tell the others. However, he thought it would be much better than being chased about by the lions, but he could not see how he was going to live among the two groups—they were dark and dirty. "You know, brothers", at last he spoke, "the valley is very large and even if the lion has forced us to live together, we can still live in groups as before, and divide the valley." The rest agreed without asking why he did not want them to live together as one group. They had better things to think about than wasting their time on that.

So the next day all the goats moved to the valley.

Most of them did not like the change, but they had to
obey the kings. The valley was then divided among the
three groups. For some time they lived happily together in
their small groups. There were no lions coming to
bother them and soon they forgot all about the lions.
They started wandering about on the slopes and even
up on the mountains. One day a lion was passing and he
helped himself to one black goat. The whole valley knew
of this and another meeting of the kings alone was called.
They all met at the black king's court to decide what
was to be done. In the end they decided to keep watch—
goats who could tell the others when the lion was coming.
At this time it was necessary to feed on the slopes because
the valley was becoming very dry. Watch-goats were
chosen from each colour. For some time the procedure
worked very well until one day the watch-goats went on
strike.

They complained that they wasted most of their time
gazing and not grazing, and that by dark they went to
bed hungry. So they decided to keep some grass for the
watch-goats. The watch-goats' profession became more
and more popular, because there was always something
to eat even when others were starving. Watch-goats were
the fattest goats apart from the kings. The black watch-
goats started to complain that the other watch-goats,
especially the white watch-goats, were not efficient: they
grazed too much, instead of watching. So the black king
sacked them, and more black goats became watch-goats.
Soon all the watch-goats were black goats. The white
goats complained, but they did not discuss the matter
outside their own group. After all they were very careful
with their piece of land: they did not graze carelessly,
like the black or brown goats. The brown goats never
complained: they were satisfied with safety and that was
enough for them; after all the blacks were very strong
and clever.

One day the black king called for another meeting.
He told the other goats that, being brothers and sisters,

he thought it very silly not to mix and have one community and one king. He told them that since God had given him a great mind with which he had saved his brothers, he believed that God had chosen him to be king over the goats' nation. The brown goats did not care at all: what they wanted was food and safety. So long as food and safety was assured them, they were ready to do anything—even to mix up. The white goats were not happy. They looked upon the others as invaders of their valley: but as they were afraid of the black goats, the black king became the king and took a private grazing-land which had originally belonged to the white goats.

During the black king's reign, goats ate everywhere, mated everywhere, and children were born everywhere. The valley was soon filled up with goats. Some goats were black and white; some were brown and black: and some were black and brown and all the varieties of colours they could produce. Watch goats too, in this wonderful time, became less and less efficient. Now and then the lion got goat's meat. It was only the white goats who were not happy with these conditions. They thought . . . the other two groups were ruthless: after we have allowed them into our valley, they go about everywhere, even forcing our white women to mate with them . . . . The others—brown goats and black goats—complained to the king that the white goats' women were not cooperative. So another meeting was called. The king was very furious with the white goats . . . . "Brothers and sisters, I am your king, chosen by God himself . . . It is time you understood that the valley and all of you belong to the nation, which is controlled and ruled by me. You are not for yourselves, but for your nation, and your nation is black, brown and white. So you all belong to one another. A brown brother is free to take a white or a black sister. I do not want any complaints of this kind."

The meeting was over. The white goats could do nothing: they were not as many or as strong as the blacks.

They could not start a *coup d'etat*. So they had to swallow
this anger and bite their tongues. The brown goats too,
having lived for years on the poor slopes with the threat
of lions now and then, took the valley and its conditions
as a retreat. They were contented and did not care
at all. The white goats wanted a change: the black reign
was too much for them. "Oh for a change", they cried,
and soon a change came.

My sister paused, and wiped her eyes with the back
of her hand and wetted her lips.She continued.

One day the former white king was very sad. He told
the others that he was going on safari. He left in the
morning, never to return. The next day his friends
went to the mountain to look for him, and what did they
see but the carcass of half his body. They went straight
to the king. The king, as usual when faced with a very
small problem, called a meeting. (He explained this as
being the nature of a democratic nation.) When they
were all seated, he gave his speech.

"I am very sorry to say that in a time like this—when
we have peace not only among the goats, but even with
lions—we have lost one of our beloved friends . . . ."

"Are you really sorry?", a white goat shouted. This did
not put off the king. "Well, brother, it was silly of your
father to go to the mountain when he knew . . . ." He could
not finish: another white goat, quite old, was trotting and
shouting "Do you know why he went? Do you know who
drove him there?" More and more white goats were
on their legs; some started throwing stones everywhere,
and soon they were copied by the black-white goats,
then the brown-white goats, and the black-brown goats.
Soon the whole valley was filled with stones in the air.
They fought one another, brother against brother,
mother against children, fathers against wives and
children. They were all blind with fighting. And what
were they fighting for—freedom?, peace? My sister
paused. I was not quite sure whether she wanted us to
answer her or not. Of course she was the one telling

the story, so she should know . . . . Well, she resumed. It could not be freedom: they had freedom already. So was it peace? No, it was change they were fighting for. They were already bored with the peaceful life.

Suddenly a tall thing, covered all over in red except for its feet, came strolling towards the valley civil war. The goats did not take heed: they went on fighting. The tall thing drove them forward, away from the valley. "—sh—shi—shi", it cried. The goats moved on, still fighting, and they were driven away, up the mountain and down the mountain, in the valleys and up the valleys. They kept on moving, still fighting. You can guess what the thing was and where it drove the goats. That is the end of my story." Everybody laughed and I did not think I could guess what drove away the poor goats or where they were driven to.

I did not like the end of the story. It was not the kind of ending I was used to—"and there they lived happily ever after." "Where were the lions?", I asked my sister, "Why were they not there to help the goats and save them from the tall thing?" My sister laughed, and told us that the lions were on the other side of the valley, laughing at the goats. She told us that the lions thought it was funny to see them being driven by a single thing crying "—sh—shi—shi". Then she added, "well you can never tell with lions—they are so mysterious, nobody can understand them. They always laugh when we think they should not laugh." I was so sorry for the goats that something like a stone came from inside me and stopped in my throat. Saki, who was always too tall for his age, stood up, as it was his habit to always show off. He started strolling from one corner of the room to the other, imitating the tall thing crying "—sh—shi—shi". Everybody laughed again; I also tried to laugh, but it only came out in a cry, relieving my throat. I could not stop my tears; this time they streamed down my cheeks, and I thought . . . "How cruel of the lions . . . . Poor goats, they are so much like us . . . . so helpless."

PETER SONGA, whose poetry appeared earlier in this book (see pp. 21-23), describes in *The Intruder* a meeting between an educated student and two uneducated Masai youths; the two very different modes of life are briefly sketched and, in the last paragraph, doubt is gently poured over the student's dreams of "civilising" the self-sufficient Masai.

The intruder

Engaruka spread out before him like a shallow bowl. Sitting on a crag on top of a dome-shaped hill, he was like a fly sitting on a lump of food. Behind him was a wall of mountains, to his left continued the plain, broken only by the dark form of an extinct volcano some five miles away, looking like a sleeping giant. Far ahead was another chain of mountains looking blue and hazy. Behind those distant ranges lay an unknown world. To his right, the almost endless flatness vanished on the horizon, shimmering as far as the eye could see, only occasionally interrupted by a tree, or the neck of a giraffe.

The basin was like a hot bath in the afternoon heat. The air trembled with a brightness that dazed the onlooker. Everything was harshly brown except for the fresh green strip of oasis describing the course of the river. Tumbling through a narrow gorge in the wall of mountains behind him, the river cut a straight course until it reached the lowest point of the plain, before it began winding its way in great loops into the glaring lake.

Mungo caught sight of two brown figures coming from the left, the direction of the river, carrying what looked like bundles of reeds. Each held his spear in his right hand while with the other he balanced his bundle on his head. Masai: he could not mistake them. They were probably carrying the reeds to the *manyatta* lying below the hill a little to the right. About a mile ahead, a column of dust hung in the air. He could see dark figures making their way to the glittering lake.

The two Masai were coming up the hill, having laid down their bundles of reeds, and were carrying only their spears. He felt uneasy. What could be bringing them up here? He calmed himself and increased the volume of the transistor radio set beside him—they might get interested in the music. Presently he could hear them panting behind him; he turned round and smiled at them. They smiled back, exposing their coppery teeth, and said cheerfully,

"*Jambo, bwana!*"

"*Sijambo. 'Abari gani?*" he ventured, in his best Swahili.

While the tall one was still agape with wonder, the short one asked, "Are there cows in Dasalamu?" which was another way of asking whether the people there had anything to live on, and to live for.

Yes, there were cows, he replied, but they were mainly kept in large houses before they were killed by a *chuma* for meat. Only a few people near the city kept cows Most of them lived on rice, maize-flour, vegetables.

They went apart and exchanged words between themselves for a while.

"That man is speaking from Dasalamu", said the tall one, pointing at the transistor set. Mungo was glad he was not asked how a man from "Dasalamu" could have his voice heard in a box so far away. They asked him to make the box sing in Swahili. He could not find a song, but he came upon one reciting a *Shairi*.

"Is that how they sing there?" asked the short one.

"Yes." He did not want to elaborate.

At that moment they heard a droning sound overhead. It grew louder and louder. Presently they saw a gleaming aeroplane gliding across the sky. Mungo's friends were following its progress in complete absorption, mouths agape, eyes agoggle. This was one of those rare, curious things from the other side of the world that occasionally visited their world. Like Mungo, it was an intruder.

As he observed them intently watching the 'plane, Mungo wondered whether the young Masai was not generally becoming interested in leaving his "native" regions to see a bit of the outside world. Only the previous evening he had been told (at the mission school by the river), of a young man who was being stopped from continuing his studies. He had done very well in his Standard Eight examinations, but his parents and the Masai elders had gone to a witch-doctor to ask him to cast a spell on the young man, so that the "madness of school" should get out of his head.

Mungo could see a new eagerness in the eyes of these two young men. That they had not been to school, he could not doubt. What would they want to do, say, in Dar es Salaam? Where would they live? Who would protect them against the vices of that world?

Here on the plains, a little thorn-prick in your flesh hurt all the family. There you were responsible for everything you did. Yes, sooner or later, Engaruka would be touched by a new hand, and all this would come to pass. How long would it take before Engaruka was a city? A hundred years? He could not tell. Yet one day the cow would become fatter on this plain than it was then. And, instead of being served by man, it would serve man. The Masai would be his own master, and then .....

"*Motokaa!*", one of them nearly shouted, pointing down the hill, at an object raising a trail of dust half a mile away. Mungo recognised it as the Land Rover coming for him. He smiled.

"*Wananchi*", he said, "I am going. The *motokaa* has come for me. I am very pleased to have met you. I hope we shall meet again."

They smiled broadly and hoped that he would travel well. They wished he could stay a little longer among them. Would he please accept a gourd of sour milk? They could fetch it quickly. He thanked them but said he and his companion had a long way to go, and must

hurry. Another time he would take the milk. He gave the tall one some coins to buy *pombe*, a local type of beer which he had had the evening before. He hurried down the hill, clutching his radio set under his arm, and waving to the two Masai. They watched him go.

Back in the Land Rover, Mungo's mind was fertile with ideas. Here was a place to transform. The river could play a wonderful part in the plan. Engaruka could be a new place—green fields, large cattle stalls, a meat factory; electricity—new roads—hospitals—amusement parks—a sprawling trading centre. With money, and people's efforts, it could be done. Let him be given the mountain for his own mansion, from where he would watch all these things happen on the plains. In ten years it would be possible—

He was rudely awakened from his dreams by the sudden halt of the vehicle. He was surprised to see that they were already half way up the escarpment. Below them spread the deep, flat-bottomed bowl that was Engaruka. The hill that he left half an hour ago was just a visible pimple on the flats. He wondered whether his two Masai friends were still there.

JOHN KIBAKI was born in Nyeri, Kenya, in 1936 and studied in Nairobi, Dar es Salaam and York. After graduating from Dar in 1968, he worked for a Publishing Company and is now an Assistant Librarian in the University College Library in Nairobi. His long story, *The Gambler's Son*, is a sensitive and perceptive account of the adventures of a young boy whose father, an unsuccessful gambler, uses his son to pay off his debts.

The gambler's son

Saturday night again! I shuddered. How I dreaded these Saturday nights! For this was the day when father returned from the big city. He never came alone, and he never came home sober. These were nights of gambling and arguing, sometimes leading to bitter fighting among the half-dozen participants.

My mother had cried and wrung her hands as her household was smashed in the fighting. She had looked, in shocked silence, as her pots and pans, and even the grain in the little round store, were gambled away. Father had long ago lost the two goats and a sheep that had warmed our hut. Indeed he had given away everything that the winners could carry. Mother bore all this in silence, and she continued to till her little shamba. At least we had food. But now the final blow had fallen. In a desperate mood, father had staked her shamba . . . and lost. This was the last straw. Mother, unable to stand it any longer, had secretly disappeared from home.

Kamau was my father's name. Everyone called him "*Wamwega*"—the generous one. Whenever he won at cards, he gave away his winnings in great carousals. Everyone in the house made merry. That is, except mother. For reasons I had never understood, father was never kind to my mother. He would give her a meagre five shillings and harshly tell her, "Woman, you don't need more. You have your shamba."

And mother had to take the five shillings, if only to escape a beating.

On this particular Saturday, things were extremely serious for father. He had lost heavily, and his debts had accumulated ominously. He had nothing left to give away. He walked about like a dazed animal, his eyes vacant. His last old coat hung from his shoulders in tatters. For some time now he had not been visiting the market lest he should meet his creditors. If people called at the house, I was ordered to tell them he was away in Nairobi, or he had gone visiting, or he was at the market. All the while he lay low in the thick bush at the back of the home.

But he could not dodge for ever. That Saturday evening, after father had stealthily returned to the house, we heard a knock at the door. With a sinking heart I opened it. There were three men standing outside. When they asked to see father, I recognised one from his voice as Komu, the most notorious gambler in the district. I knew that my father owed Komu a lot of money.

Father went out of the house. After a few mumbled words, the four of them walked away into the dark night. Now I bolted the door, for I was afraid of the night, and for a long time I lay on my bare bed and trembled. Then sleep overcame me . . . .

Kamau and the other three walked through the dark, heading for their favourite den under the fig tree. There were two or three lanterns shining feebly from the low branches. A group of shadowy figures sat in a circle under the lanterns. As the newcomers arrived, there was a stir in the group under the tree; they called out greetings and invited Kamau to sit and play.

One of Kamau's escorts was the master of the local gamblers. The gamblers' code decreed strict adherence to certain rules and obedience to the master. No one dared question his word. And now he spoke:

"Comrades, you know our code. When you lose honourably, you pay up. When you win honourably, you keep. Comrade Kamau here lost to Comrade Komu. But he did not pay. Instead, he has been hiding himself, as if he could escape our brand of justice.

"Komu here has appealed to me. And he has made an offer which you shall hear now. Stand aside."

The master paused. When the men had moved aside, he called Kamau and Komu to the centre of the circle of light. He addressed Kamau:

"Comrade Kamau, you have been one of us for a long time. Never before have you betrayed us or refused to pay. Whenever you have won, you have been generous. We do know that you have nothing now left to pay up with. But pay you must!"

"Your house is too old. Your wife is no more the girl she was. But you have a son."

At the mention of his son, Kamau raised his head as if to protest, but the threatening look in the eye of the master stopped him. The circle of ragged men stirred. All eyes were turned towards Kamau. The leader continued:

"You have a son, Comrade Kamau. A robust son. But Komu has no son. Indeed he has not been blessed with any children. Now Komu offers you a chance to regain honour—and freedom. You stake your son in a final game with Komu. If you win, you keep your son and your old debts will be forgotten. If you lose, Komu will take your son, and, of course, your debts will be forgotten too. Do you accept the challenge? Your choice is between this and the obvious alternative!"

Everyone, of course, knew Kamau would lose. But they had to go through the ritual.

Kamau, looking very frail indeed, tried to speak, but no sound came from his mouth. Then at last he sighed, a very long-drawn sigh, as if his heart would break, and said:

"I'll stake my son . . . my son . . . !"

77

For a few moments no one stirred. Then the master spoke and a mat was at once spread on the hard trodden ground. The group got into a circle again round the figures of Kamau and Komu.

Komu looked aggressive, but Kamau had somehow shrunk. Defeat and resignation could be seen in the drooping shoulders and the hands that shook as he took his cards.

They played for a long time. No one spoke. Only painful sighs broke the silence. They came from Kamau as he saw his adversary's heap grow ever higher.

Now Kamau held his last card—his trump. His eyes were set and vacant. Perspiration rolled down his face. But he uttered not a word.

He threw his card. Komu threw down his. Kamau had lost. Of all games, he had lost this one. Yes, he had lost; not only the game, but also a son, his only son!

———

There was silence for a long time. Then the master said:

"You have lost, Comrade Kamau, honourably. You have lost a son. But you have regained honour among us. You have bought your freedom."

Kamau said nothing. He stood up. Now he did not shake, as if desperation and a sense of finality had brought him calm. But there remained a nagging pain in his heart. As always when he lost to Komu, he felt he had been cheated but could not prove how. He could not argue. No one argued in these matters.

After a long pause he offered a hand to Komu and said: "You come for the boy tomorrow . . . ."

———

"Son. Son. Wake up now."

For a moment I thought I was dreaming. The last thing I remembered was father leaving with the gamblers and I bolting the door for fear. But the voice insisted. "Son. Son . . ."

I jumped in bed, rather frightened. That is father—I told myself, trying to still my fear. But how did he get into the house? Then I remembered we had that secret hole in the mud wall through which one could unbolt the door from the outside.

"Yes . . . . Yes, father."

"Wake up now, son."

"But father, so early?"

"Yes, son. You are going on a little journey."

Of course it was not the first time father had sent me on errands, some long, some short: to the market, to the in-laws and even to the other gamblers' houses. I did not question that. But why was this so early? Why did father sound worried?

While I looked around for my little cloth cap and my stick (they said a man never travelled bare-handed) I could hear low voices from just outside the door. When I emerged I found, to my great astonishment, that it was Komu. Komu again? What did these men want? What did Komu want now?

As I stepped out Komu advanced towards me, saying: "Son. My own son now."

I could hardly understand. Was he drunk? Or mad?

As he tried to place his hands on my head I cringed and held back. My little fists tightened involuntarily. What did he mean, calling me "son"? Father now intervened:

"Don't fear Komu your father. You know he is my *wakine*."

There was a pause. I knew what father meant. A *wakine* of your father was your father too in the clan; but only symbolically.

"You know your mother has left us, son", father continued.

"There is no food in the grain store. There is none in the shamba. Do you want to starve? No. We shall not starve together here. Komu, my *wakine* will take care of you. He has no child of his own, and he has a large shamba and many sheep and goats. His wife is a kindly woman. His land is far, but it is a land of plenty.

"Go, son, go with your father Komu. He will be to you what I have been."

I stood there aghast, my mouth open in wonder. This had been a terribly long speech for my father for when he was sober—which was not often—he spoke little. And now he sounded so unusually kind!

I could hardly believe my ears. Was father giving me away? Was he sending me away now? Surely not! Though he drank and gambled, there remained an untold bond between us.

I had loved father somehow. Now I pitied him. For the first time in many days I cried. I cried as only a brave boy can cry, for throughout all the bitter days I had not cried once. Not for hunger, nor for fear; not even for the long lonely days. I cried now because I could see . . . that my father was suffering too. My heart ached for him when I saw his eyes were closed, and his brows knotted with strain. I knew he was crying—inwardly. Even Komu, the mysterious Komu, had averted his hard eyes.

How miserable I felt! I was as ragged as father, if not more so. I now wore no shorts. Only an ancient shirt, torn along the seams at the sides. Its tails flapped like great wings when I ran. My bare feet were cracked and dusty. But above all I was hungry, hungry as never before. How wonderful it would be to eat again!

The thought of hunger somehow stopped my crying and I turned my eyes to the hut that had been my home for so long. Now it looked lifeless, dark and cold. It had not really felt like home since mother disappeared.

Momentarily all the wonderful memories of my childhood flooded back. I looked beyond the hut to the thickets where I had had my hideouts. I looked at the tree I had loved to climb, and the patch of grass where I used to sit and sing to my little flock.

When I turned and faced the two men I could not fail to notice my father, bare-headed and now grey, with sunken cheeks and a drawn face. He wore shoes no more. His clothes appeared even worse than I had imagined. He avoided my eyes. He seemed to be looking far, far away, as if seeking a glimmer of hope, a redress for all these ills. But the look in Komu's eyes was different. There shone some kind of triumphant malice, exultation.

I had stopped crying. Indeed we were not used to much crying in my father's house. Komu now spoke.

"My new son, it is not right for men to cry. Come with me without fear. There will be plenty to eat and to drink. You will never go hungry again." (Why did they have to torture me with the thought of food?)

"You can look after my flocks and play with all the boys in the neighbourhood. You need never be lonely again, my boy. And I shall give you two lambs for your own. Njumbi is a wonderful place, and your fa . . . . and Kamau here can always come to see you."

I had heard of Njumbi. I knew it was a very distant place. But had not father assured me? Surely he would never give me away. And if this Komu did as he said, it should be a good place to go to.

We walked slowly down the path that led to the distant road and the market. When we came to the road, father stopped. He looked at me and stretched out his hand. We shook hands. He seemed to choke with emotion as he said to me:

"Goodbye, *my son*. Go you well. I shall see you again soon. Very soon."

He emphasised "son". Perhaps he was reassuring himself and reminding everybody that I *was* his son.

Then he turned to Komu.

"Goodbye", he said simply. He did not shake Komu's outstretched hand.

When we parted I did not dare look back again for fear I should cry and run back.

By now the sun was up. It was warm and rather more cheerful. How I remembered this road! Had I not run along it a thousand times, skipping and jumping, when father had sent me to market? Had I not dallied to play in the dust with the local shepherd-boys? Today was different, I thought. I did not quite know where I was going.

_____

For the first time I found myself observing Komu closely. Up till then he had been simply one of those men that came and went with father, to me merely one shadow among others. Probably because he was not a fighter (too clever for that) I never noticed him particularly. Now, however, I could not help looking closely when I thought he was unaware. But he caught me at it.

"What are you goggling at me for, son? Hurry up, or it will be high sun by the time we make the market."

I turned my eyes away quickly and pretended I had been only looking at the distant hills on his side of the road.

Komu now walked just ahead of me and to the right. I thought he looked sleepy or drunk, as his gait was wobbly. On a second glance, however, I found the cause. His legs were thin, too thin, and they tapered down to feet that were twisted grotesquely outwards. It must have been the jigger when he was small. I knew boys who were like that. If the little parasites were left to grow freely on the tender feet of children, they caused horrible sores. Victims walked through life with out-turned feet, leaning heavily on their heels.

Poor Komu, I thought. He could hardly keep up with me. When I obeyed the order to "hurry", it was not long before he was calling again, now from behind me.

"Why are you running?", he complained.

I was not running at all!

_____

Soon we neared the market. A great roar like a waterfall was borne to our ears. The hundreds of voices of haggling men and women were all rolled into one vast roar. It never failed to excite me, visiting the market. What boy of ten would miss the thrill! The bright kerchiefs of the women; the variegated wares; the jingling of the bells from the livestock area; the sweetmeats all around one! Invariably there would be a juggler or two who greatly amused us children. And of course there was the old man who wore a skin cloak, as he recited the *gichandi* epic for public entertainment.

Lost in this reverie, I was rather surprised when my escort said sharply:

"This way, son. Don't you see? We are going to the shops."

The seriousness of my situation returned to me now. In my excitement I had forgotten that this was not one of my usual errands to the market. I could not tell where Komu was leading me. But I was not too worried yet.

First we went to the cobblers. Komu said he had left shoes there for repair. When these were produced they were not shoes in the real sense. They were coarse military boots that many people bought from returning soldiers. Komu examined the heels of his boots. I could see where scraps of motorcar tyres had been fitted to correct the worn-out corners of the heels.

Now Komu paid the cobbler and promptly put on his "shoes". They hardly corrected the angle of his misshapen feet. We went on.

Next we called at a small grocer's. My boyish spirits rose when Komu ordered sweets for me. He even bought a bottle of that sizzling liquid they called "soda". We boys had often seen these bottles, but could never afford one. I began to think Komu was a wonderful man. Why had I feared him so much? I said to myself, "If he can buy me soda now, surely he will feed me at home. And didn't father promise to visit me often?" I could even afford to smile at him when he said:

"You are hungry now, aren't you? Let's see the butcher."

The butchery here was simply an open space some way behind the line of ramshackle shops. The men slaughtered their animals out in the bush. Here they brought strips of meat which they hung on crossbeams erected on the spot. The meat was covered with long, green banana leaves as protection against the flies. But those indomitable insects somehow found their way: they buzzed everywhere.

At a little distance from the hanging meat, open fires had been lit between rows of large stones. Over the fires were arranged thick green branches on which to grill the meat. Lengths of delicious sausages were also cooked here.

My stomach rolled with anticipation when the aroma of the roasts assailed my nostrils. How hungry I felt now!

After a little haggling, with the butcher moving his greasy knife along the top of the sausage with deliberate measurements, a proper length was agreed upon and Komu bought it. I thought it was the longest I had ever seen bought in one piece. They wrapped it in a length of dry banana bark. Then Komu told me:

"Take this, son. I'll show you where to eat it."

I could hardly contain myself for joy. Sweets, soda and now sausage! It's a great day, I thought. But my happiness was to be short lived.

Far back behind the line of shops was an abandoned shack. It was half hidden behind a large fig tree. Komu now led me there. He said I should remain there so as to eat my sausage in peace. But I feared to be left alone in a strange place. When I tried to protest, he nearly shook my head off. He raised his voice:

"What are you up to now? Don't you want the meat? P-o-o-r, s-i-l-l-y b-o-y . . .! Do you want to go back and starve?"

He was fuming.

I knew I could not go back. Where? I had no home now. I remembered how, during the last few weeks,

I had barely existed on raw sweet potatoes dug up from mother's old shamba, bless her. Since I no longer had any animals to tend, I had had all the day to roam the nearby bush, hunting for wild berries. What father ate I did not know, though on a few evenings he brought home a piece of raw meat. I had a childish notion that grown-ups never really went hungry the way we children did.

Somehow I had managed. But now, with the succulent sausage in my hand, I felt such an acute sense of hunger that it was akin to pain. I asked Komu:

"Where are you taking me, *mzee*?"

"Don't call me '*mzee*' ", he growled. "Call me 'father', do you hear?"

After an angry pause he said, a little more calmly:

"All right, son. Don't worry. You stay in here and eat your sausage. I shall soon come back for you. Don't try to run, or the devil himself will get you."

With that he opened the wickerwork door and pushed me in. It was so dark I could hardly see my feet. I thought I heard him fastening the door from without. And certainly when I tried to pull back the wicker, it was fast. Some vague fear, a kind of premonition, assailed me. Why had this man called me "poor, silly boy" in that sneering way? And why this lock-up?

But I ate. I ate the whole sausage. Then I lay on the earth floor and, telling myself not to fear, dozed off.

I was awakened by a great commotion. The door opened with a crash and several men rushed in shouting. "*Kihii, Kihii*", they called. "Where are you? Get up."

Several hands roughly lifted me off the ground. They hustled me outside where they tied my hands together with a wetted strip of dry banana bark. I noticed their leering stares and winced. They were drunk! Or mad! I began to tremble and tears welled up again. But I should not cry, I told myself. Who was there to help me anyway?

"He's a tough one, eh ?", one laughed.

"No tears, brave ?", another added, pinching me hard on my backside.

Now I could not stop myself. Bitter tears gushed. I wailed. I howled.

"Where are you taking me ? Leave me. Leave me alone. Oh my father, father. Oh Kamau. Who will help me now ?"

I continued wailing.

All this time the three men were dragging me along a bush path that led down the hill away from the market. Then a terrible blow caught me on the mouth and I staggered.

"Shut up, monkey", one big man shouted.

"Did you call Kamau ? If you ever mention that name again you will be skinned alive."

I was whimpering. My nose ran freely. There was blood on my bound hands. Yes, I had been hurt. I could taste blood.

"Who is your father now?", asked the big man.

"Mmmm . . . .", I mumbled. I did not want to say "Kamau" lest they killed me.

"Who is your NEW father, you fool ?"

Now he really sounded furious. But I still refused to answer. Indeed I could not more than mumble because of the violent whimpering, and the swelling lips.

"WHO IS KOMU ?"

He raved and foamed at the mouth. His eyes were those of a madman.

"My father's *wakine*", I answered innocently.

"WHA-A-A-T ?"

With that he slapped me so hard that I fell flat. He stood over me now, one booted foot poised as if to smash my face in. His two friends stood around—laughing! I was thoroughly scared. Fortunately this brought me to the sudden realisation of what the devil wanted me to say: that Komu was my father. Now I knew who they were: Komu's accomplices. But why were they so cruel ? Surely it could not have been upon Komu's orders.

"Komu is my father", I now corrected myself.

"HEAR, HEAR," the others shouted in chorus, slapping their hands.

"Say that again", commanded my tormentor triumphantly.

"My father", I said.

"Good boy, brave boy. I knew you were not a fool. You had only forgotten, hadn't you?"

"Yes, yes", I answered quickly.

Now he pulled me to my feet. I could not rise by myself, my hands being tied.

"You will not forget again?" It was more of a suggestion.

"No", I promised.

We walked in single file down a narrow path. Two men led while the big one, the one who had beaten me, followed behind me. We came to a small river across which was laid a single log. It was the bridge. The two men crossed first, balancing themselves by spreading their hands. I knew I could never get across with my hands tied. So I said to my guard:

"Won't you untie me so that I may cross?"

"NO. Go right ahead, you swine."

"But my hands! I cannot balance. I may fall in. I don't want to drown."

I was pleading now.

"GO ON", he shouted. "Don't waste my time. Can't you see it's late?"

But I still held back. Impatiently the man shoved me forward onto the log-bridge. For a frightful moment I tried to keep my balance. It was too late. With a wild yell I slid from the log. I saw the fast stream below me. I thought I was finished. Then two strong hands held one of my legs as it left the bridge. And there I was, hanging upside down by one foot, the other dangling away in the air. The swift water was just below my head. I was yelling. Then I was dragged, feet first, back to solid ground. I lay there panting, hardly able to see. My head was whirling round and round. There was a sound of running feet, coming across the bridge.

"What do you think you are doing, Rua?", I heard a voice shout angrily.

My tormentor murmured something. Now I knew who he was. Rua was a name I had heard among my father's gambling-mates.

"Do you want to kill him?", the first voice demanded. "Do you want Komu to hang all of us? Haven't you tortured him enough already? Get off, you skunk! That stuff you smoke will drive you mad yet."

There was the sound of a violent scuffle, followed by a loud thud. When I looked, Rua was lying flat on his back, his booted feet high in the air. Despite my pain and fright, I could not help feeling gratified by the turn of events.

"Here, brave boy, get on my back." This was one of the two men who had returned from across the bridge.

So I rode pig-a-back across the river.

Now we were only three, the two men and myself. Rua must have found it wiser to return to the market.

We walked up a sharp hill. At the top we turned into a side-path and moved deeper into the bush. The brief misadventure and my rescue had momentarily bogged my mind. But now I remembered. I was a captive. I might never see my old home again.

Before I had time to worry further, we came to a clearing. To my great surprise Komu was there. Komu, my "father", was there, obviously waiting for us.

"You are late", he said calmly.

"*Ndukamake*—don't worry, Komu. We have delivered the goods, haven't we?"

"Where is Rua?", Komu insisted.

"That hyena?", exclaimed my carrier. "He went back. We let him have one or two at the river. He nearly got the boy drowned."

"What?", Komu demanded, turning to inspect me. "And why is the boy's face swollen? Tell me, you devils."

"*Ni Rua*, it's Rua", they chorused.

I could see the two were afraid of Komu. This was hard to understand since Komu was so frail. After a tense pause, Komu dismissed them.

"Alright you two. Go back now. I'll see you and Rua when I return. But he would be wiser to move on sooner", he concluded ominously.

He handed them some paper money. They left.

——————

My hands were still tied although Komu did not seem to notice. Or perhaps he didn't care. So I said to him: "Won't you untie me now?"

"No, son. We'll leave it until we reach my village so that you may be washed too. If we untie them now, they may get cut and I don't have oil to put on the wounds."

This sounded so reasonable that I could not question its wisdom. But I wondered why he would not at least inspect the hands first. I kept quiet, however, because a funny little idea had begun to form in my mind.

——————

Now we were two, my "father" and I. I led as we walked along many paths. Then we came to a hill. From further up the slope I could see a village to the left, far below us. Smoke rose in lazy spirals from the thatched cones of the homesteads. It was now getting towards sundown.

As we walked further in the open we could feel the heat. My banana handcuffs were painfully tight now. I looked down at them. Then it struck me what my funny little idea really was. Of course I could not run with my hands tied. But the banana bands were now very dry. How easy! We walked on and on, in silence. When we came to the top, Komu suggested we rest. I agreed gratefully, though not only for the fatigue. We sat on two adjoining rocks, facing away from the sun. I waited.

To my great surprise, Komu began pulling off his old boots. Poor man, I thought. He had actually been limping up the hill. What a chance now! Komu, without his boots and with feet so badly blistered, would be hopeless in pursuit. I waited.

Now his right boot was off. He was struggling with his left. The laces were knotted tight. He cursed under his breath and pulled harder, but his fingers continually slipped, being wet with sweat.

All this time I held my breath. I pretended I was watching the struggle, but all the while I was straining at my bonds. I could feel the dry fibre slowly, ever so slowly, giving. I considered my captors had been drunk. Their knot was so carelessly done.

At last Komu's left boot was coming off. I let him pull a little more until his foot was half out. Then I did it.

I jumped up with a terrific yell. At the same time I broke off the last cords of my bonds. I was now on my feet, running free, flying down the hill the way we had come.

Somehow I could imagine my "father" struggling: first to recover from the shock my yell must have given him; then with his left boot, half on, half off, and one blistered foot unshod.

I was flying now. I did not care. But I heard his cries, his curses. They followed me down the hill, though I could hardly make out his words. I heard only scraps: "... stop ..." "... you and your father ... hang you both ..." "... accursed ... play with Komu ... gr ... rott ...."

I heard no more. Presently I was at the bottom of the hill. I dared to turn my head. O God! He was coming. Komu was actually running down the hill. Yes, he was limping his way down, boots in one hand, stick in the other, with the old coat flying out behind. I had probably

91

underestimated him because of the crooked feet. But wasn't he a grown man? And me a mere child of ten. His stride would be worth two of mine in any case. Oh dear me, I thought. The sun beginning to set too!

I had now reached the smoother bush-paths. They branched this way and that. If I slide behind a bush along a side path, I might escape Komu. He would come thundering by, along the main path. By the time he had discovered his mistake I should be able to get a long way off along the side path. I did not know where it led, but anything was worth trying to escape the wrath of this man.

All these thoughts merely flashed through my mind as I raced down our path. Suddenly a side path appeared ahead, to my right. I jumped into it and after a few quick paces slid between two thick bushes. There I lay low.

Komu came thundering (or should I say "pattering"?) down the main path. He was still yelling and cursing, demanding that I stop. I saw his coat flash by. Yes, flash! I had not realised he could run like that. But I did not stop long to wonder.

I hesitated a moment, unsure of where to turn. Then it flashed through my mind that the village I had noticed from Komu's hill was in the direction of my side path. I started running now, harder than before, for there was hope ahead.

I ran and ran, twisting round the bends in the un-familiar path. I dared not stop, though my lungs were nearly bursting. I felt I was getting weaker, but I pushed my legs farther. I forced myself on and on until I began to cry because of the strain. I thought I should never reach the village. But I ran on.

Now I could run no more. No! I must die. Let Komu get me now. It is better than this. It is better than death. I do not want to die.

Now I was falling, falling. O God, I was hitting a bush. No! I must lie down. I must.

These were half-conscious thoughts that fiitted through my fevered mind. I could not stand more. So I collapsed, there beside the path to the village.

Dimly I thought I could hear voices: men's voices and women's. I thought I even heard children playing somewhere; or was it boys dancing the *muthuo?*
I am dreaming, I thought. But then there was a fire. I could see the glow and I felt warm. Was that a face looking down into mine? How kindly it looked. It was a woman's. It looked like mother's face. Oh mother! Am I dreaming? I must be dreaming. Or dead. Let me sleep.

I closed my eyes to shut out that kindly face. It could make me cry. Oh no! That could not be mother's face. She had gone away. She could not know I am dead, somewhere beside a path.

As I was dozing away again, a voice came to my ears, very clearly now.

"Reke akome", it said. "Let him sleep now."

I sat up. This could not be a dream. That was mother's voice. No doubt now. No other voice ever sounded so kind.

"Mother", I cried aloud.

There she was! She came running from the fire.

"Yes, my son. Yes, Chira wa Kamau. I am here with you. Do not be afraid again. My son, my own son, my only one."

"Mother".

I was crying now. She cried too and our tears mingled as she held me to her breast.

How wonderful it was to be with mother! How warm it was to *have* a mother again.

She told me the next day.

Two men who had been herding their flocks in the fields near the village had heard the crying and the

93

running along the western path. At first they thought it was nothing much, since herdboys often fought and ran about crying. Then it struck them that it was rather late, the sun having set, for anyone to be coming home from the direction of the hill—and crying too. So, when the crying and the running stopped suddenly and for no apparent reason, they decided to investigate.

They left their flocks in charge of herdboys and started to walk towards where they thought the crying had stopped. Then they heard another sound. A grown man was also running along the same path in the same direction. He was shouting and calling:

"Stop, you. I'll get you yet."

One of the shepherds had said to the other:

"Hurry, man. I can sense trouble."

Of late there had been a growing animosity between their village, Muhatio, and the next one, far over the hill. It was, therefore, possible that a Muhatio boy had trespassed on the other side. Retribution was usually harsh: very, very harsh sometimes. Hence a boy running and crying. And now a man obviously bent on no good.

The shepherds hurried along the path. Soon they heard the sound of beating, accompanied by a man's voice.

"You thought you would get away, eh?" (A blow.)

"You son of Satan." (Another blow.)

"You'll pay for my lost boots." (Blow.) "And my bleeding feet." (Blow.) "And my torn coat." (Blow.) "And my . . . ."

They listened no more. They ran. In no time at all they were on the spot.

"Stop beating the boy", they ordered.

"Who are you? This is my runaway son."

"Son!", the two scoffed. "You would kill your son, eh?"

"That's none of your business. Get away."

"Oh no we shan't", answered the dauntless shepherds

in chorus, as the stranger advanced towards them with a raised stick.

Blows were exchanged. But the impostor was no match for the hardy shepherds. He was soon bound with creepers. While one shepherd led the now cowed man, the other carried me on his back.

"You were hardly conscious", mother told me. "But you managed to tell them who you were. That is how they knew you were my son. You didn't know, but this is my aunt's village, your own great aunt, and they know me well. This is where I came when I had to leave you alone . . .

"Now eat, my son, there is plenty. You will never starve again.

"Yes, Komu is well known. He is in good hands now. They escorted him to the government *boma* this morning.

"I also sent for your father this morning. He should be here by sundown.

"So eat now, my Chira, there is plenty. You'll starve no more."

R. NG'ETHE

RALPH NG'ETHE comes from Kiambu District in Kenya and is currently a Law student in Dar es Salaam; his work has previously been published in *Zuka* (Oxford University Press). *So There* is a brief look at the brazen and hard-hearted city-girl; the author has avoided explicit condemnation of Jo's antics and indeed has actually succeeded in making the reader pity the desperate, blind and fragile life of the story's central character.

So there

Jo lay on the grass and gazed at the stars. She felt that feeling of sublimity that defied identification. The world was really a very good place, if only you knew how to get the most out of it. She pitied the many girls who passed day after day only half living. They went from boy to boy, insincerely or genuinely professing love, playing at sex but never obtaining real, lasting satisfaction from it.

No wonder they were frustrated in life. Boys had so little to give. They came steaming hot but their hotness was so quickly dissipated. If only the girls knew. A man of about forty—such as Stephen—was just the thing. He was inexhaustible. His range of experience was incredible.

"In this one month I've known Stephen I've acquired enough experience to match the pros. My future husband should be most grateful to Stephen, if he ever knows.

"Ah, my parents, the poor dears. If only they knew. Would they ever believe it? But what do they expect me to do—live in utter dullness? How can I be a religious fanatic at twenty? I bet at twenty God was the furthest thing from their thoughts. How else could they have ever met? Anyway I was born within seven months of their holy wedding."

Jo let her mind wander over her past. It had all started

when her oversexed cousin had seduced her, when he was supposed to have been helping her milk the cows. That was long ago; they were both about eleven or twelve. The incident at twilight behind the cowshed led to others with primary-school classmates. Jo had made a discovery. On to high school and the adventures became bolder. Also alcoholic drinks came into the picture. The crisis came when she and another friend were driven back to school one Sunday evening by rich boy-friends. They were drunk and late for the parade. They were rewarded with suspension just before their School Certificate Examination. Her parents were stupe-fied. They could not try to imagine what had become of their daughter who taught Sunday School during her vacations. A forgiveness in the Christian spirit followed Jo's bath of tears and penitential prayers. A change actually came over her.

She turned her back on love affairs with boys. This was because, as she told Janet, boys were so unsafe: anything you did with them was bound to come out. And they were so self-esteemed, and over nothing at that. So Jo told Janet to forget her recent heartbreak over a boy who had deserted her. Jo took hold of Janet by the nose and pushed her into the hands of Martin Muloki. Muloki was a Mkamba. To Jo, no self-respecting Kikuyu girl should have anything to do with a Mkamba. But then Janet was so childish and silly and, worst of all, prone to falling in love; so Muloki would do well for her—and he also happened to be Stephen's constant companion.

Jo and Janet had been brought together by sharing a room in the hostel, as they were studying together in the Secretarial College. Jo didn't quite know what made her take it upon herself to become Janet's guardian. She didn't stop to think about it but simply attributed it to her generous spirit which impulsively made her help others. Janet was extremely pretty. She looked precisely what Jo had earlier expected herself to become: slim, tall, graceful and coy. But the reality had failed to match the dream: Jo was each day growing rounder, and there was too much flesh about the knees. She was not tall. In fact, one of the reasons why she disliked boys so much was that she had come to know they called her "banana"— presumably a fat, very ripe, yielding banana.

Jo had met Stephen Nderitu at a wedding party during the first week of her stay in the hostel. He was with his wife—a rustic-looking specimen of a woman. Mr. Nderitu looked utterly bored with his wife who just sat drinking bottle after bottle of Fanta. He gave Jo the impression of a man running away from his wife as he danced away with different women. Jo was dancing rather intimately with the best man when somehow they became entangled with Stephen and his partner. A whispered word between the gentlemen and partners was exchanged.

Jo playfully pushed her thighs against Stephen. He responded only slowly—it seemed. It was only slowly that Jo discovered that something was happening to *her*. It was as if she was being swallowed in an emotion she didn't understand. She found that they were at quite another end of the large room. There was a door and Stephen led her out. Then he held her and she felt his power break forth unreserved. She felt like a very tiny body in an immense and powerful sea which could toss and throw her about at will, and in whose infinite power she was drunk. Her blood screamed for more of it; she craved to be drowned for all time in the sea. But all Stephen said when the kiss was over was "I'll come for you at the hostel tomorrow at seven". And he left her out there. She was no longer sure who was the hunter and who the victim.

Today her parents had come to see her. They were happy she was turning out well. When they drove off, Jo hurried back to her room and changed quickly. Janet was ready and impatient. They went out to the men, who were waiting outside in Stephen's car. They drove

away, one of Stephen's hands guiding the car while the other went on a mission of exploration over Jo's body.

The car stopped outside the "Acacia"—or, rather, just before it. The girls scurried out and the men drove up to the entrance. The girls walked round to the back of the nightclub, and Martin opened a side-door for them that gave on to a dimly-lit garden. There they joined Stephen.

They knew their corner well. They had been here many times before. The waiters usually kept it free for them on Saturday nights. Stephen and Martin were shareholders in the club. Janet liked the "Acacia": it was yet to be invaded by the "people from home".

The drinks came—whisky and soda for the ladies, beer for the gentlemen. They all filled their glasses and toasted themselves.

Jo sipped from her glass and looked sideways at Stephen. She resisted the urge to jump into his lap. She asked instead, mockingly, "How's the madam and kids?"

Stephen laughed scornfully. "They are fine. Madam is not terribly cooperative these days. Must be suspecting something. Insisted on coming. I slapped her—you know, for discipline. She locked herself in the bedroom, saying I needn't trouble to come back. She won't open." He snorted.

"Oh, you maltreat her", said Jo, with symptoms of admiration. She leapt into his lap and threw her arms round him. She kissed him hard, thrusting her tongue deep into his mouth and shaking violently. Stephen tilted her backwards and thrust his hands under her blouse. The bra snapped. He pulled it away. He cupped in his hands the young, fattish breasts which were nearly lost in folds of soft flesh. Jo sobbed in ecstasy. Her hands, acting on their own, started tearing away wildly at Stephen's clothes.

From the other side of the table, a muffled moan told Jo that Janet was a step ahead.

"Hey, Jo, let's go and dance", Janet whispered in Jo's ear.

"What?", Jo said, sitting up and removing grass from her hair. "Have you gone out of your mind?"

"I think it's all right. There's nobody who knows us there—I looked."

Stephen came up. "It's all right, Jo", he said.

"Oh, okay", said Jo, standing up. Suddenly she didn't care. She felt in a reckless mood. She smoothed her skirt and rearranged her hair.

Janet held her hand and Jo pulled it out with a snappy motion. Sometimes Janet irritated her beyond endurance. "Love—Bosh!", Jo said spitefully. "Disgusting."

The problem with these girls who have grown up being good, Jo reasoned, is that when something snaps the damage is irreparable. Janet was so preoccupied these days with her hunger for men that her studies were suffering. While Jo, whose life was one long escapade, knew how to share herself among her affairs.

The girls slipped into the arms of the men and went into a slow waltz. Jo was leaning her head on Stephen's shoulder and feeling wonderful, preliving the night ahead, enjoying each second. The floor was crowded. Somebody stepped on her foot and apologised. The voice made her look up.

She came face to face with Peter.

She felt herself freeze in Stephen's arms. Everything seemed to stand still.

After an age of paralysis, Jo freed herself from Stephen's arms and fled to the toilets, her mind in disarray.

Peter was just in time to stop her from closing the door of the lavatory behind her. He pulled her out by the arm. She put a stern, rebuking look on her face, and started to point out that gentlemen were not allowed into the Ladies' Toilet. The words died on her lips. Peter did not look as if he would allow such preliminaries, aimed at inveigling him.

"What's this?", he demanded crisply.

Jo looked squarely at the tall undergraduate. She
admitted to herself that she liked him—could have
loved him if love were not reserved for the weak-headed
type like Janet. There was something about him not
found in the run-of-the-mill boy.

"It's my brother-in-law", Jo articulated.

"Your what!", Peter thundered, looking taller than
ever and quite a terror.

"I mean—my uncle", Jo stammered, in utter confusion.
She bit her tongue: ought to have remembered that
Peter knew she was the oldest in her family.

Peter looked wild. He shouted at her, calling her a
slut! He flung Jo away from him. She banged into the
wash-basin and held on to it. Peter started advancing at
her. She tried to contract into the basin. Then Peter
stopped. He swung round and marched out, cutting
through Stephen, Janet and Martin as they came in.

Stephen moved forward and the stunned Jo collapsed
thankfully into his open arms. So that was that,
she thought. She had lost something.

She had become involved with Peter to save Janet,
whom Peter had been making a beeline for. But she
found herself, afterwards, unable to free herself of him.
She discovered she didn't want to. He was so respectable,
incredibly uninterested in sex, and only working on a
long-term plan leading to marriage. Jo had come to
respect him; she didn't see herself ever marrying him,
but she felt so at home with him. So far he had believed
in her. And now this!

Presently Jo pulled herself together. "I'll be all right",
she said. "Please leave us!"

The two men left. Jo looked around and saw Janet
clinging in the corner, whimpering. Jo lost her temper.
'You're just like him, that son of a whore!", she rasped
out at Janet. "How presumptuous can people get! What
does he think he is? He doesn't own me." Her voice
was rising.

Suddenly tears were running down her face. She

stopped herself from screaming.

"So he'd dare place himself on the same level as Stephen, would he?"

Well, Peter wasn't exactly on the same level with Stephen. He had no car, nor did he have enough money to spend on her.

"He called me a—", she screamed, "—a *slut!*" She spat out the last word, indignantly.

Her wrath spent, Jo looked at Janet, who had all the while stood nodding and speechless. "Fool!", Jo yelped at Janet. She wheeled round and walked into the dance-hall. Stephen and Martin were waiting just outside the Ladies' Toilet. Jo grabbed Stephen by the arm and told him they should leave.

They started moving towards the exit. Just then Jo noticed Peter drinking among a group of men. She moved over, pulling Stephen along. She glared daggers at Peter, who calmly went on drinking.

Jo lashed out: "You don't own me, hear? I'll do precisely what I like with myself—and you can go jump over a cliff and see what I care. So there!"

Peter did not once look up, nor did he give any sign that he was the one being addressed.

Tossing her head from side to side like a proud un-broken mare, Jo resumed her march to the exit. She told herself that she did feel elated: she had told that nosey bastard where he got off. She told herself that she was longingly looking forward to the night ahead in a motel-room. She *had* to enjoy it as no other night, if only to celebrate her victory. She did not hear the talk about "these sluts" that rose in her wake. She did not notice that Stephen's step was uncertain and uneasy. She was not aware that Janet and Martin, who were following, looked sheepish and ashamed. She did not know that she herself felt defeated and lost.

The will of God

"Oh, my God!" Hamisi cried bitterly. It was not over his mother he was crying, he was crying after visualising the barrier of mystery awaiting him ahead. He drew his cap to his fore head, covered himself with self-pity, and sat on the mat which reminded him so much of the past. This done, he tried to figure things out. It was useless. He was the unluckiest boy the world ever found. He sobbed bitterly and regretted his birth. It would be better if you remained in the dark world unborn where you would experience no difficulties—or better still, be born and die and go to that peaceful and quiet land of the dead, rather than live in this world of miseries crying throughout. He swore and cursed his parents for bringing him into the world and then leaving him alone with such difficulties. The grief of his mother's death was not in his mind. She had followed her husband and had gone to rest. They live happily there—in the land of the dead . . . .

Between Morogoro Road and Titi Street, there were renting houses. In these houses the tenants mingled and lived together. The houses were mud-walled and tin-roofed. Those landlords who had enough money had had the walls of their houses plastered but not many were plastered. The houses were built many years back and now they had lost their beauty and were old. They looked as if they would not stand very long—still there they were: year in, year out—desolate, dilapidated and very dirty.

The tenantry included Africans, Arabs and Indians.

These were not rich but neither were they very poor. They lived together like brothers and shared their poverty and troubles regardless of colour. The tropical heat tanned their skins so that you could not distinguish an Arab from an Indian—you could not tell who was who. In the evening, the tenants gathered and sat at the corridor where it was somewhat cool. There they chatted and exchanged views freely and happily. When the "three" men were alone, nothing could stop them from discussing women. And the "three" women on their part derided and despised men—or rather pretended that they despised them—the whole race of man for his roughness and clumsiness, when they were alone, despite their colours.

When the time of prayers came, these tenants mingled and prayed together because they were all muslims and had the same faith.

People who passed here on their way to town, saw these old houses and shrugged their indifference. And so, the little village remained alone and nameless not on the side of town and not on the side of the African locations either; filthy and ruinous. And the houses, ever inclined to fall, and showing every sign of their not wanting to stand any longer, still sheltered the mingled tenants.

In one of these houses, at the end of the corridor, there was a little room. It was the first thing you discerned as soon as you entered through the corridor door. The room was built after the whole block was built. You knew this not by being told, but by the way the room stood its ground and the boldness it showed. It showed every sign that it had nerve enough to live even if the other rooms collapsed—but, nevertheless, it was dirty and stinky like the others. In this room lived Juma and his wife, Rehema. If you entered their room, you at once realised that they were poorer than the other tenants. Their bedding, their utensils and the way they dressed were enough to convince and leave you with no doubt that penury had really got the best of them, and you had but to pity and sympathise with them. But they didn't like sympathisers. Many a people had sympathised with them and it didn't buy them anything. They were as indigent as before. But this time, though poor, they were happy because, after long, dreadful years without children, Allah seemed to hear their prayers and had given them two—a boy and a girl. In their prayers, they always thanked Allah for His consideration and justice.

Juma was a fisherman. He was heavily built, short and had rickets which made his legs look bow-like. When he was in business, he wore a piece of cloth, like the others, which was run between his legs and then was wrapped around the waist. When out of business—which was rare—he wore *kanzu*, long trousers, and a coat—and then the cap. Thus dressed, he would then pick his way to mosque for prayers. His wife, whose beauty was wearing out, was charming when she was happy and interesting when she was interested. She would keep the whole family laughing for a long time with very interesting stories and riddles which she told with such conviction that she always made them sound true. For example that one of a man who slept under a tree with his mouth widely opened. The snake came and knocked at the door (the unshut mouth) and when there was no answer, it found its way through the mouth into the stomach. Once there it never wanted to come out again because of the delicious food it got—and people called it intestines. When this snake bears children when they come out, people call them tape-worms. Sometimes when one eats bad food, when the snake tastes it, it grumbles and twists uncomfortably and it is then that one says that his or her stomach is eating him.

Rehema, by telling such stories, could warn her children against eating bad food like mangoes which are not ripe, and being very careful not to swallow a fish bone because, as she said, this snake is very naughty and is not appeasable.

Like a devoted muslim woman, she wore *buibui* always and this made it hard to tell whether she had many clothes or not. Their daughter, Mariamu, was twelve and was giving all promises of beauty. They dressed her as nicely as they could because she was their pride. People saw her and admired her. And the young people shook their heads enviously when they met with her.

Hamisi, their son, was a boy, and so they treated him like one: an old pair of shorts was enough for him. He need not have a shirt; why, with all that heat—after all, weren't the boys meant to go naked? A pair of trousers, and old, white shirts, and a cap were always kept in the box for him to wear during the "Idd" ceremonies. Juma didn't have enough money to pay for his uniform and fees. But he could afford to supply them with fish. And so, they ate fish and lived on that.

Foreigners came from different corners of the world and saw these welcoming, determined people of Tanzania and liked them. As soon as he arrived, the former didn't hesitate in associating himself with the latter in his heavy task of building his poor and immature nation. And Dar es Salaam gave them peace and warmth. It protected them and comforted them. They became happy, and called it "haven of peace"—because it was quiet there.

Hamisi took to his father and grew up strong and active. He appeared bigger, wiser than his age. You had to guess his age—even his father had to. There was no correct record of his birth kept. At the age of fourteen or thereabouts it occurred to Juma that his son was big enough and it was time he learned how to work and depended on himself. So, he began by taking him to the sea on some of the short trips they made in their boat. Some turbulent waves, the ceaseless sea breeze and the burning of the fierce sun would add something to the boy's masculinity and would make him a tough character—the father thought. The boat belonged to three people, and when Juma brought his son along to join and help them in their fishing, the two comrades showed great pleasure—because they were sure the boy would demand no salary. Juma didn't mind. His aim was to teach his son something. Something that would help him in his living days. But, poor, old father, if only he could foresee the coming days; if only he had a little knowledge of the nature of the future awaiting him ahead, he would have taught his son how to fish earlier. But then, if he was equipped with that fore seeing power, he wouldn't have been a man of this world. He would have been different.

It was one of those "Idd" ceremonies she was coming from. There was some quarrel between her and her mother earlier. Mariamu wanted to go to those ceremonies alone but her mother had told her to wait for Hamisi who had gone fishing with his father and who was expected that evening. "I am seventeen and I can take care of myself, mother. Look, I am not even going alone. There is Mwajuma, Hadija and Sihaba and they are not going with their brothers, mother. I shall join them and we can go together. Nothing will happen to me, mother." Mariamu argued with that burning teenage boldness, pretending to be wise and big.

"I don't like that", the mother negated. "You have to wait for Hamisi and he will take you. I don't trust those girls; they are not clean." "No mother. I have to go! You can't treat me like a child! No! No!", she sobbed. Rehema, being rather tired of the argument had gone out of the house and Mariamu, no sooner had her mother gone out than she had started to prepare herself to go. She washed hurriedly, put one or two touches on her well-plaited hair, powdered her face and then picking up the *khanga* and wrapping it around her shoulders, she was out of the house and into the crowded and dusty streets on her way to Magomeni—the dancing centre.

It was night when she finally decided to go home. The traffic was not very heavy on the road and along the path, just one or two people she happened to meet.

Most of the people were still at the ceremonies, but she had decided to leave earlier lest her mother should have a heart failure if she stayed out long. And just as she came panting along the deserted path, something, of which she was naturally conscious, happened; four big and strong blokes appeared in front of her, almost from nowhere, and blocked the way. Their faces, which were masked, made them quite undistinguishable. Slowly, they started advancing and she started retreating. Then, suddenly they seized her by her arms roughly. She screamed with fear, but nobody was near to answer her call for help. They covered her mouth with dirty handkerchiefs. She kicked and twisted with all her might, but to no avail. Then they slapped her face and cheeks hard; they blinded her, and before she passed out, she heard them mention her name and say, "beautiful girls like you are hard to get these days, Mariamu, and when we happen to come across one, we treat her like a respectable lady. We mean no harm to you, and if only you . . . ." she heard no more.

It was the next morning when she stirred and showed signs of life—on a hospital bed. Her parents and her brother were standing there, quietly watching her. It was the mother who broke the silence by asking her how she was feeling. Then slowly and craftily, in a most motherly way, she asked her what had happened. Mariamu burst into tears, helplessly. They waited patiently for her to quieten, but she could not control herself. Finally, the words which took ages to come out of her mouth and which seemed to burn her like fire, were suddenly blurted through sobs "they . . . they . . . ra . . . . they *raped me !.*" . . . Silence ensued. The whole ward was as quiet as a grave. Slowly, without a word, the father shook his head with feeling. Nobody to blame. It was the will of God. He turned his eyes to his daughter with self-condemnation and guilt. Fate always has its way. She was no longer a—a proud virgin. Never again. Everything was different now. But whether a virgin or not she was still his only daughter. "It is the will of God," he found himself saying, unaware whether his words were audible or inaudible . . . . The nurse came and ordered them out of the ward—they were disturbing his patient.

After a few days in hospital, Mariamu recuperated and was permitted to go home. She didn't want to go back home because things were no longer as before. Her parents would be different, her friends would ridicule her and she would be the laughing stock of the whole village. But then she had nowhere else to go. She had to bring herself to face the shame, nasty and foul as it was, because it was her own fault. If she had heeded her mother's warning she would still have been the same proud and beautiful Mariamu. However, things were not as bad as she had thought because her parents were sympathetic and everyone else seemed to understand her situation.

But after three months—three months? No. Rehema had known it all along but had kept and locked the secret inside herself. A capable mother should know these things naturally. When a daughter starts selecting her meals, plus those constant stomachaches, a clever mother can tell at once the matter with her daughter. In this case, Rehema was no exception and it needed only a doctor's test to confirm Rehema's thought about Mariamu's pregnancy.

A mother is always trusted to show and teach her daughter how to behave with the opposite sex and when a thing like this happens, it exposes the mother's incapability and in many cases the father is likely to fight. So Rehema lived in fear these days—more so because her husband had adopted a keeping-quiet habit ever since that day things began to take the wrong course.

Juma sat on the stool and opened the door to let in fresh air. If you looked at him, you thought he had already had a shower in the bathroom because he was all wet—but with sweat. As soon as he had finished his meal, Hamisi had gone out for a walk, leaving the rest there. None of the three had spoken yet. Juma, who appeared to be under a great strain, turned slowly and faced his daughter, whom sorrow and sadness had seized and whose body was growing weaker as time passed away. "My daughter", he broke the stillness, "now, supposing you tell us who this proud father is." He said that abruptly then kept quiet and watched the effect of his words. Mariamu didn't cry this time. She had cried enough within those past days.

"I don't know him", she said curtly. The fact was inescapable. "It only happened that day they took me by force and no more." This was followed by very awkward silence. The father moved his eyes from his daughter to the floor. He sighed regretfully. This was the last hope he had. At least if there was this father of the unborn child as he had fancied, he was prepared to squeeze him and get something out of him, but things were different now. In his mind he saw the beautiful castle he had built slowly begin to tumble down, one stone after the other. He looked from his wife to his daughter, without so much as letting out a single word. He was done. But was he done forever? No. There is always hope. One can't just merely give up like that. Allah the Creator was still alive. The daughter was still his and whether pregnant or not, he could not just throw her away like mere garbage. Besides who knows, things might turn out good. Nobody knows tomorrow. He turned vigorously and faced his daughter who, by now, was crying quietly with self-pity. "It is all right, my child. Don't cry. We will see this thing through, all of us together. And don't forget that it was not your fault." Rehema, whom fear burning fiercely, heard these words and they converted her: her hatred of her daughter was dissolved into love. The fear in which she was living disappeared and she found herself comforting and consoling both the father and the daughter. And then the time of prayers came and Juma, adding to his daily prayers, asked from God

Almighty forgiveness for the wicked thought he had entertained and asked him to give him more power to look after and guide his poor family like before.

Things went on smoothly from then on. Juma supplied his family with fish as usual and always urged Mariamu to eat more than before because they were now "two in one"; Rehema nursed and cared for her daughter in a motherly way, giving her instructions and showing her how to behave like a woman. She comforted her and kept away the fears which naturally confront young mothers like Mariamu. Mariamu in turn responded and obeyed faithfully like a good, determined young mother who is being introduced to the mysteries of the world which have existed ever since it was created and which she herself could hardly see before she had reached this stage of mother-being.

Days slowly slid away, and with time, peace and happiness almost reigned forever—but not before a piece of bad luck struck again.

Mariamu began vomiting after her meals and then agonising stomachaches followed. Sometimes, when one of these excruciating pains seized her, she would stand still, open her eyes widely and then tighten her jaws so hard that the veins around her face would thicken with blood. This dreadful, momentary process would last just for a short time and then she would come out of it wet with sweat. And the panic-stricken family, seeing this, would go down in prayers.

Then followed terrible bleeding and they were compelled to take her to the hospital. But it was too late; Mariamu miscarried and, to everybody's surprise, died in the hospital. And the family realised with much pain how much Mariamu meant to them and how dearly they had loved her. Rehema mourned her bitterly with motherly and womanly love, and for two days, she hardly ate anything. After the funeral, the three stayed indoors, sharing the grief sorrowfully; the reminiscence of their daughter came into their minds relentlessly.

Rehema was no longer the charming mother. The impact of the blow was rather too much for her. Hamisi was withdrawn and dull. He had lost his only sister in the world. Sister with whom he was brought up and lived, and sister who always made him feel like a boy—sister whom he will never see again in his days. He cried bitterly as he remembered some of the jokes they had shared recently. His mother saw all this and pitied him. And after the moaning and bitter days were over, she changed his name and called him "Liziki"—an only child.

Heaven of Peace was not disturbed or pestered in the least. It generated peace and warmth as usual, and consoled its occupants. She reared her mingled residents faithfully, like a shepherdess, despite the terrible threat-to-fall of the walls and foundations of the houses which time and dirt had almost eaten away.

One day, Hamisi insisted on going fishing with his father. Like any other boy, he wanted to entangle himself with the mysteries of the world. After his sister's death, he was compelled to stay home with his mother. Now he was tired of staying home all the time. His father consented at once, and off they went in the waters. The fishermen cast their net into the sea as usual; the net found its way into the deep water, trying to attract as many fish as possible. But no real fish dared come near it—not what fishermen call fish, at all. The day ended and the night descended, and the fishermen were still in the sea with their net in water. Hamisi was starting to regret his joining them. He was cold and, above all, there were no mysteries as he had anticipated. But at dawn, something happened. Two big sharks were caught in the net, at last. The father shark with his madam, as they said, had come for their breakfast but, unfortunately, due to the sharp, morning appetite, had landed on the wrong table which was reserved for the guests and, at any rate, they were in for it. Their struggle began. The sharks got mad and began to fight their way out. The fishermen, very happy with their big catch, grabbed their paddles and began to beat the sharks to death. The father shark got mad and began to charge in all directions, pulling the boat along as it charged. The more the fishermen beat them the more the sharks got mad and ran. Juma felt excited. To demonstrate his efficiency, he stood up and went to the far end to fasten the net to the boat much tighter. The boat, as it were, tilted and unfortunately somehow frozen, Juma lost his balance and fell into the cold water. He swam professionally but was unable to reach the boat. His comrades threw him a rope as a last resort, but the mad sharks, surged with dreadful pain, pulled the boat forward as fast as they could and the rope failed to reach Juma. Hamisi looked at his poor father swimming helplessly with furious waves sweeping him backwards. The boy screamed with fear, but in the circumstances he was of not much help. Juma swam on, fighting the horrible waves. It was a competition—a swimming competition between him and the sharks. But the spectators, regretfully, were beginning to see the winner. Soon the competition will be over. The winner will march away victoriously and the loser . . . the loser? They kept quiet with fear of the inevitable; their mouths open and their eyes agoggle with wonderment. They waited for the obvious. And with feeling, they watched and witnessed the competition abruptly come to the end: they heard him scream and saw a bloody wave sweep over him. Due to experience, they at once knew—another shark was breakfasting off their comrade's body. Another sharp, frightening scream, and they saw him no more . . . . The gods of the sea give fish to the fishermen and in exchange they grab, from the fishermen anything handy, both mysteriously and untimely. They are both unpredictable and implacable, the sea gods . . . .

Rehema slowly wore her *buibui* and sat on the stool more like a corpse than a live creature. She covered her face with the black veil and buried herself in her miseries. Two whole days she had been crying and now she was tired of crying and sick. Hamisi tried to comfort her but she didn't seem to hear; she was blinded and deafened by calamities. It suited her to stay alone, quiet and cry when tears came—a crumpled heap of misery. The mingled neighbours each took his or her turn to come and console her, and as they came, each brought her a present to show his or her sincere concern in the whole situation. They cared and sympathised with her like good and true neighbours. And when finally she recovered, which took ages, the true, mingled neighbours gave her another name automatically—"Mjane"—a wife whose husband is dead.

After constant and hot complaints to the authority, Rehema was granted a temporary permit to sell green vegetables for she had no other means of earning her living. She started off with some seventy shillings which she had gained from the fishermen as a result of her husband's death. They had told her that there was less than eighty shillings in the partnership for Juma but that they were sympathetic and wanted to co-operate. So, after an incomprehensible calculation, they gave her the seventy shillings and, openly, told her that they were now through—no such thing as partnership with Juma or his son any more.

In the market, Rehema's little business was doing well. She tried to nurse it patiently, fighting with the terrible difficulties which naturally came on her way as a young inexperienced business woman who had spent half her life indoors as a faithful wife to her husband. Hamisi had to go to Kariako—that big market place—early in the morning, buy the vegetables at a reasonable price and then bring them to his mother who then would sell them at a market price.

After bringing the vegetables, Hamisi would rest for a while and watch his mother arrange them, business-like on the bench, speaking to them as if she understood them and they her. And when a customer came, she would speak to him nicely with that kind and sympathetic voice she had adopted after her husbands' death—a voice which didn't convey any commandment and which wouldn't let a customer go without buying something from her. Some didn't understand Swahili—fluently and eloquently spoken as it was—but at least they thought they understood this young and kind woman who, unfortunately, was crumpled by miseries. Hamisi always laughed when he heard some of the Swahili spoken by foreigners. After listening intently, he would then bet such people alighted from a plane not more than a week ago, because if they had stayed here long, of course they would have known more Swahili. With those professional teachers (houseboys) who demanded no pay, one could learn a lot of Swahili in fact. Some spoke it fluently, and some were even unable to pronounce words. Hamisi then finding them in such a fix, would laugh until his eyes filled with tears. But Rehema would try to teach them kindly and they would then thank her. Eventually, as Hamisi got used to these people, he learnt to teach and to welcome them. The Europeans then after being taught a little Swahili would express their gratitude by pressing something in Hamisi's hand. Hamisi curiously would then open his hand and find a shilling or fifty cents, but never more than that. Hamisi couldn't help calling them misers. "Why" he asked, "can't they give more than that? Damn them, Wazungu. They are like a Masai who locks his money inside his leather bag with a padlock; gradually the money accumulates and if you happen to meet him with that bag slung on his shoulder, you think him conductor of some bus: he would rather die than part with five-cent-piece from his damn bag."

The sun armed itself with its spears and took to its daily journey, to and fro, day in, day out, to an unknown destination yonder. And with each journey, days slowly accumulated themselves into years. And with years the old died leaving unforgettable cries behind, and the young, nevertheless, thrived happily to take their positions. This is what people call life.

Rehema, after working hard, somehow resumed her beautiful figure once again; she was attractive despite the age-lines which unavoidably occupied her face. The mingled tenants were no longer dull and haunted. They were charming, happy and grateful. Their dirty houses, which distinctly told their history, stooped with age, but still held on, clinging to their foundations like leeches, and never let go.

The day before yesterday was an "Idd Eve". Yesterday was an "Idd Day" and today as well. Rehema, naturally, had been very busy those last two days, selling vegetables to the people who bought them furiously due to the celebrations. She wisely stole a glance at her little money-bag, when people were not looking, and smiled a little because it was "bright" and was "swelling" little by little as time passed away. She smiled again with a self-satisfaction and then sat down and put her hands on her lap. She had succeeded after all; no doubt she had. It was not hard to live without a husband if you were bold and ready to do anything. If you were not lazy at all, life would be smooth and easy for you. But some other things like those sexy smiles men give you can't be helped, of course. You find yourself smiling back unawares. After all, are you not free to do whatever you please ? You are not in prison, of course. He smiles, you smile back and nothing more. What is wrong with that ? After all you don't have to be a cold-blooded creature. You have to revolve with the world. There is no harm in finding yourself a mate . . . Ah! Anyway . . . .

Now today was her day off—her first day off. She had decided to go off duty and relay a bit. Work was there always and you had to work until your day came. She over-slept that morning and relaxed on her bed. In the afternoon, she washed herself slowly and carefully put on new clothes and all the time, her heart was jumping up and down with excitement. Then she caught a bus to Magomeni for there, apart from traditional dances, she had some friends. Hamisi had left earlier after his lunch and where he had gone, she need not know. He was becoming a young man now, and it was hard to understand his movements. He is trying to be matey or something, Rehema thought. A beautiful girl has come his way and blinded him, perhaps.

The traditional dances were wonderfully performed. The dancers jumped up with joy and swivelled their waists happily. The *ngomas* went on playing, people danced joyfully. Their bodies sparked with perspiration but they never gave up. Everybody was mad; mad with joy. They hypnotised Rehema; she watched them intently. Yes, intently, of course, for she would not go back home. The dusk came and went. The twilight came and changed into darkness and Rehema never thought of going back home . . . .

It was midnight when Hamisi arrived home at last. The mingled tenants were asleep or were still at the *ngomas*. The village was quiet like a grave. The moon was full in the sky but dull. It was a mating season and here and there, a group of dogs sexually assembled. If you looked at them for the first time, you thought them to be drunken people sitting down. But if you went nearer, the dogs would bark wildly at you and it was only if you were lucky that you would escape safely without a bite or a scratch from them—which was rare. In a queue or in a group, they breathlessly ran after the sexy bitch without giving up. Fathers, sons and brothers, all ran after the female, each waiting and hoping to have relations with this sexually attractive female.

Hamisi knocked at the door, but there was no answer. The light was visible inside, which meant that Rehema was in. It gave him some unpleasant feelings and he felt cold. He took his key from his pocket and inserted it in the hole. Smoothly as usual, the latch clicked back and the door opened. Rehema was sitting on the mat, her hands supporting her head and tears coming from her eyes like rain. Her eyes were red and heavy after a long crying. The lantern on the dirty table illuminated the room with dull light. If you looked at it you saw four of them, and yet, it was just one. Everything was tampered with and disturbed. The air was not very pleasant. It gave you some bad feelings. Her clothes were torn into pieces. The dirty beddings were ruffled and some thrown on the dirty and dusty floor. Hamisi was shocked terribly and was unable to speak at first. When he spoke, his voice had another tone and his throat was dry with wonderment. He didn't know where his saliva had gone, and so his lips were rough and dry. "What is it? What is it, mother?", he asked, kneeling down by her side. But this tortured her all the more and gave her more tears. She sobbed bitterly without stopping. Scalding tears. The same sobs. The same ceaseless, bitter sobs. They were familiar to him. Where had he heard such sobs? Yes, yes, in the hospital, years back. He was young then, but he never forget. He remembered very well: his dear sister. His dead sister, Mariamu, in a hospital bed years back. She was crying and sobbing exactly like his mother now. But she was dead now. One need not think about the dead. "Mother, please! What happened?", the boy pleaded, with tears half-way. Rehema tried to speak but she couldn't. She tried again, exactly like Mariamu in her hospital bed:

"They . . . they . . . they sto . . . sto . . . they stole our money. Whole of it. Nothing they left. Nothing indeed . . . oh my God . . . Oh!". So that was it. The money had gone, leaving them naked and hungry; hungry and lost. Yes, lost, for without money, what can one do in this corruptible world . . . .

Life is strange. People pretend to be sympathetic. You think they are sympathising with you, but it is a mere sham. They are jealous and full of envy. The nasty envy of course. And as the saying, *Kikulacho ki nguoni mwako*—something that bites you must be hiding in your own clothes' goes, so was the whole thing. You see people walking, talking; you see people doing things and what is hidden at the back of their heads, what is locked in there, is hard for you to know. You can't know. And that is why all people are unpredictable. You can't predict how one will behave, how one will act. The thief must be none other than one of the mingled tenants. The possibilities are there all right. It must be a man who had known them for a long time. And a man who was sure where the mother and her son had gone. But Rehema and Hamisi could hardly suspect him. It was no use notifying the authority. Authorities are not angels; they can't reveal what is hidden at the back of the thief's head—only He, who is in heaven can do that—it is It is will . . . .

The lantern on the dirty and rickety table blinked once and as it did so, it reduced some of its light. It was tired of burning. Never like this before. They were over-working it. Either they had forgotten or they were giving it a punishment. It had to remind them. So it blinked again and reduced its light a little. Human-beings have to be just, really. The dirty lantern which was converted from a Nescafe coffee bottle, grumbled and gave its warning again. But no one seemed to mind it. "All right, if I can't get justice here, I can get it else-where", and with a put . . . put . . . put . . . . and then a choke, the tired lantern took its dull light away and went to sleep, leaving the room totally dark, haunted and full of ghost-like shadows. But the proud lantern was in dire need of kerosine; it was dry and hot like a radiator. And with one good crack which divided it into two, it was a lantern no more. Nobody moved or showed any concern. They were there in the dark room quiet like a cemetery, each in his and her own thoughts, and more dead than alive . . . .

He must have slept—slept? He even had over-slept. Oh, sleep is such a crazy thing! It catches you unawares even in moments of sorrow like this!

It was around eight o'clock when he awoke. He had
not meant to over-sleep. He had not even meant to sleep
at all—not after what had happened. He had covered
himself on the mat, his head resting on his knees and his
hands on his cheeks and his eyes open. But sleep had
seized him and he had fallen on the mat unawares like a
drunken man. He had automatically covered himself
with cold until his whole body was in the form of a
question mark. And now, as he awoke abruptly, his
joints, which were used to the question-mark form,
did not want to change—they were painful. Every part of
him ached terribly. His head was going round and he
felt sick and weak. He opened his eyes with an effort
and tried to come back to reality. And, as he wandered
his eyes around the room he saw it. He thought it was
standing there alive. It bore no alteration; nothing had
changed at all. The dress she was wearing yesterday,
the *buibui* the bangles, the *mkufu* were all on her
person. He called her, "Mama", as he usually called her,
but there was no answer. The sweet and reassuring answer
he always got from her was no more. He opened his
eyes a bit wider, and then he saw the thin, strong, black
wire which ran about her neck. The wire which took
her life away, and the wire which had made him an
orphan child. It was tied around her neck. Her hands
vainly clung to the dirty wire. When she saw death
coming to her, she had vainly tried to hold the thin and
cunning wire with her hands, but it was of no use. The
hands never moved from the wire: they were now stiff
because rigor mortis had developed. Her tongue, half
out of her mouth, indicated the toughness of the fight
she had against death. Her eyes, half closed with sorrow,
showed distinctly the strain she had undergone. Her feet,
stretched with much pain, told very well that she wanted
to reach the ground, which was not more than three
inches, but to her, it was miles away and she died before
her feet could touch it. The floor beneath her was wet
which indicated that she had urinated with pain—and

there was her whole stature, stretched in full length, dead and stiff with *rigor mortis*.

When people suffer a great shock, they don't feel it just at first. If your hand is taken away from you, you don't know for a few minutes that your hand is gone. You go on feeling it, and your fingers. You stretch and beat them on the air, one by one and all the time, there is nothing there, no hand and no fingers.

Hamisi did not believe that his mother had committed suicide. He did not believe that his mother was dead. He just sat there, staring at her as if she were a picture. But he was not seeing her. His brains had some other important things to think about. Things like his new girl-friend whom he had met only twice. Things like the broken lantern-bottle which lay in halves on the floor and some other irrelevant things which his eyes came across. It was too great a shock for him, but it had not yet got the best of him . . . .

"Oh, my God!", Hamisi cried again bitterly. The shock was affecting him slowly like a disease. He saw things now. He saw his mother distinctly hanging there on a wire; he saw clearly the barrier of mystery awaiting him ahead. His mother's corpse was there all right but she, herself, had gone to rest. She had run away from this wretched world and had followed her husband, who being tired of the insatiable family, had preceded her. They had gone to rest, of course, both of them together . . . .

He sprang up suddenly; he threw his cap on the floor with anger. He paced here and there, stamping his feet ponderously on the floor, his eyes out of their sockets, and his lips tightened with rage. He was finding something; what was it? Yes, there it was—the stick. He picked it up with irritation. Rehema had gone, of course, but she had not carried her body with her. He was going to beat it until it screamed with pain—no! Until his anger was appeased; until he felt good and happy. She can't die like that and walk away with it. The boy started beating the corpse angrily. The corners of his tightened lips became white with foam; he was drenched with sweat, but never yielded. The stiff corpse swung from side to side and it was only when it fell down that he stopped beating it. Lying there on the floor, it had the real air of a corpse and Hamisi was frightened. It now gave him the creeps and made him sick. He threw the stick away quickly, guilty, like one conscious of something, and wandered around the room trying to avoid the sight of the corpse. He was like a trapped animal; his condition was hateful and fearful. He didn't know what he was doing and all the time he spoke to himself his eyes widely opened. Then, by chance, he saw the door which was still shut since last night. With one jerk, the door—which had longed to retire for a long time—gave way and the mad boy bolted away. Then he came back again. He had to lock the corpse in lest it should get out and follow him. And after fixing the door—which took just a few minutes—he was off into the streets. He ran on, raising his head and twisting it like an animal smelling danger. He ran into a car and it almost knocked him down, but fortunately he was on his feet again. The drivers complained angrily: "He is a new boy in town, straight from the shamba" they thought. Hamisi never heeded them. He ran on and on without stopping. Something was chasing him of course. It was always on his back and he saw it. What was it? Yes, the corpse of course. He wouldn't let it catch him. No. His mother had warned him against corpses. She told him that corpses are dangerous things; they can convert you into a dog or a pig or anything they wish. That is why he was not allowed to see his sister after she died. And now this corpse was following him; he had to run away from it and escape with his life. Was he insane? No, he didn't know. You don't know when you are sane or insane. Insanity is like sleep; it catches you unawares and all the time, you tell yourself that you are normal; that you are sane. But you are abnormal and insane and you don't know it. The other people know it by your symptoms and behaviour—your behaviour gives you away . . . .

Along the road he ran until he came out of town but he never yielded. The corpse was always behind him and he had not to give way to be turned into a pig. No! A true muslim like himself was not to be connected with a pig. The sun burned fiercely and the boy sparkled with sweat; his lips stick-dry; his feet dusty and sore, but still he had enough courage to run on. A mad person is stronger than a normal person; the former can do without food longer than the latter; Hamisi didn't feel hungry; the storm broke and the rain washed his tired body and massaged it passionately; it gave him more power to run on. Over the ridges and across the plains he ran. "Hamisi, where are you going?" "Away from the corpse; it gives me the creeps." So, the boy ran away and there was no coming back ever.

Haven of Peace was disturbed. Every soul was agitated. The mingled tenants squimed uncomfortably. The little, dirty village was alone no more: the people who happened to pass there on their way to town never shrugged their shoulders again. They stopped and pointed out to each other: "Do you see that dirty, stooping house over there, old man? There, yes, it is there where she was found after her five-day absence, throttled to death with a wire—the poor Mjane, you know. And, do you see that road over there? You call it Morogoro, don't you? It is the one the boy followed to his grave—her son Liziki, you remember. They don't know where he died but he is not in his world—this corruptible world of ours. It is the will of God, my friend. He has the power to make things fall apart."

F. N. BARASA

Christmas day

It was another Christmas and along with it came all kinds of enjoyment and good things. To Komu Christmas was a great day. Last Christmas he had been ten, and this Christmas he would undoubtedly be eleven although he didn't know the exact date he had been born. He had obtained information from his father when he was seven that Christmas comes round after one year. "This is your seventh Christmas, my son", his father had said. "You are seven years old you know. Another seven Christmasses and I will have a big he-goat." Komu had been young then and he hadn't known what his father, Njoroge, had meant by "Christmas". He only bore in mind that he was seven years old and that every Christmas represented one year.

Komu's mother was the first wife and so she had all the responsibilities in the home. She was his father's right-hand wife. Komu, as the first-born, was given the privilege of going to greet his father every morning, before anyone else. His father had ten wives and lots of cows and sheep and lots of servants. Komu wanted very much to look after his father's cattle, but his father had sent him to school, keeping him away from the animals.

The morning was warm with some mist when Komu woke up to prepare himself for the day which marked his eleventh year. He hurriedly put on his pair of shorts and khaki shirt, yawned, and then unlatched the reed-made door, being careful not to let the sheep out. He ran in the direction of his father's hut, half-blind with unwashed eyes. His father was snuggling on his hide bed, under which had been placed some sticks to represent a pillow. "Father, are you well?", asked Komu apprehensively, kneeling down. His father, whose left leg was chopped off at the knee, slept with his crutches beside him. What had really chopped it off, Komu never knew and he dared not ask!

"Ahmmm! Ahay!", his father sighed, and then yawned. "Komu, go to your mother; tell her to go and call our neighbour, Kuria, at once and tell him to come with his sword and his spear! Then tell her to come back at once and not to go and sit down there! From there go to your stepmothers and tell them to each bring her fire wood rope at once. Do you hear me?"

"Yes, father." Komu left quickly, before his father could notice that he was grumbling. He began his journey. He was in the seventh hut when his step-brother, Ndicu, laughed at his unbuttoned shorts. This infuriated him. He started cursing his father in his heart. "That one-legged old man! He is so stupid! He has given me such a hard job, going round his village, calling his wives so early! Old fashioned . . . ." "Can I keep you company?", asked Ndicu, who was naked, despite the old calico sheet wrapped around his shoulder which was so dirty you could say it was dyed. They all respected Komu because he was wearing a pair of shorts and a shirt, and because he was their eldest brother. "Yes, let's go", answered Komu, who always showed his bigness to his step-brothers. Before they left, Ndicu pinched Komu on the shoulder. Komu frowned questioningly and then he saw what Ndicu was showing him. Under his mother's bed were two big heaps wrapped around with sacks. Around the fire were six of them and the fire was not very big. Komu nodded. From his experience he at once knew that it was *njohi*, wine, in those big gourds. They were covered so that people might not goggle at it and stop it from fermenting. That one under the bed was ready; all you needed was to swallow a couple of gulps and you were drunk. That one near the fire needed but a little time. It was making some noise and on top of the gourd some bubbles were visible which indicated its unreadiness and that it could not make even a boy dizzy.

They went on together, calling their step-mothers and passing on their father's word. "So that is where they hid it?", Komu asked Ndicu on their way back. "Yes", Ndicu answered. "There are no sheep in our hut, and father says it is safe from everything, even rats, and he . . . ." "Hey! You naughty boys!", the father yelled. He was coming from his hut, hopping on his crutches like a kangaroo. "If you are told to do something, you can't do it, eh? Just like your mothers!" The father was now hopping towards them. He thought that they had not conveyed his message to his wives. At once Ndicu wanted to dodge and run away, but then he remembered that his father had said "boys" in the plural, not "boy", and he knew that he was involved. He didn't like the way his father pinched their ears as a punishment, but he couldn't escape. The two boys waited, fear eating into their flesh like vermin.

"Go and bring me my whip! Quickly, eh! You . . . you . . .." Then he caught his words, and remembered something and then slowly he relented. He must not do any fighting or anything bad-tempered during this day. If any neighbour happened to hear him, he would be called in front of the elders of the tribe and Fate knew what would come next.

The two boys came with a which whip was made from a giraffe skin and which the father used when teaching his wives lessons. "Go to that tree; cut as many branches as possible, and then put them there." He pointed towards the most central of all his huts. "Be nice boys and obey your father", he said kindly, with a voice whose politeness shocked Ndicu who had been expecting a pinch. He hopped back to his hut and met Kuria whose strength and ugliness personified the character of the baboon. With him he had his sword, drawn from its sheath.

"What seems to be the trouble? Wife run away?", Kuria asked curiously. "Simmer down, my old friend",

Komu's father reassured him. "You're always there whenever I need you—you are my left leg, you know!" Then he stopped. The two boys, who had been standing there all the time, hidden merely by air, ran away quickly, before he could see them. They had brought twigged branches and the father and Kuria arranged them on the floor so that they made a big bed. By then all the wives had gathered together with their firewood ropes, and sons and daughters had gathered too. But no one dared help Komu and Ndicu with their work. Komu gave them a hostile look and whispered to his companion, "I tell you, you cheat yourself if you think that you can beat them at eating: they really know that game! But when we come to work . . . Phooey! They are as hopeless as a fifteen-year-old donkey, take it from me." Ndicu, who was not bothered by his nakedness, said, "Perhaps we'll be given some reward. I could manage very well with some sour milk and . . .." "Stop it now, my boys", the father shouted. "That is enough! I wouldn't beat you now! We are friends: you have had your punishment alright." Ndicu frowned with anger, but before he could say anything he saw Kuria coming from the cowshed followed by a big bullock. It was the fattest and the biggest animal in the herd. Ndicu brushed Komu's shoulder and murmured, "They want to kill it. You'll be given the sweetest meat. We've been working together since morning you know, and nobody helped us. We're hard-working boys, don't you think?" Komu again showed his bigness, shrugged his shoulders, and kept quiet. And from then on Ndicu followed him wherever he went.

Kuria tied the animal's front legs with a rope and then ordered one of the women to hold it for him. And, to show his competence, he started making a sweet tone by whistling softly and stroking the animal reassuringly. The animal was very familiar with this tone and, for an answer, it stood erect so that Kuria was able to tie its hind legs without any trouble. Then suddenly, with women helping, he pulled the ropes and the animal fell on its side with a bang so that Ndicu almost ran away. Komu's father was hopping around restlessly, making cracking noises with his tongue, until Kuria signalled him to come and cut the animal's throat. With a very sharp knife, Komu's father hopped towards the animal. The animal saw the glittering knife and naturally knew their plan. It started twisting and kicking helplessly for its freedom. Komu's father laughed and, pointing at the animal with his knife, hopped with his one crutch and said, "Eh! Stay still there, I'm coming. Only one blow and then we are friends. You won't even feel it, or I'm not Komu's father, Njoroge the one-legged giant." The animal kicked more than ever, made a queer sound and, as Komu's father neared its hind legs, broke through the rope. With one good kick which Njoroge didn't even feel, he found himself on the ground with his thighs far apart. Kuria sprang to the animal before it woke up and the women ran to their husband's rescue. Ndicu laughed at seeing his father on the ground, so Komu gave him a sharp pinch which cut his skin and said, "You mannerless little fool, shut your eyes. Don't you dare look at his nakedness!" Ndicu, who wanted to revenge himself, frowned and then shut his eyes as the pain ran through him. And when he could keep them shut no longer, he opened them to find his father cutting the animal's throat and saying to Kuria, "You see the disadvantage of having women around you, and the advantage of having you here? They just stand there, staring at you with mouths open as if you were a picture. If my Komu had been stronger, that animal wouldn't have kicked me."

With the help of the boys, Komu and his companion being the first, Kuria skinned the animal. Komu's father sharpened some sticks to roast the meat with. He was humming quietly and then suddenly he said, "I should have known better than to castrate that animal. It has broken my crutch. It wanted to revenge itself. Really it almost castr . . . ." Then he caught his words and looked at his children. "Come here, all of you!", he shouted, to hide his embarrassment; and then he ordered each child to go and call the neighbours. "Tell them to come with their wives! Do you hear me?" The children— some making the sound of a motor-bike, some the sound of a heavy-loaded lorry, and some making the sound of a racing car—ran off, each imitating the driver's behaviour, and disappeared, in different directions, into the mist.

"Wairimu!" Komu's father called Ndicu's mother, in whose hut the *njohi* was stored. She came running, with some firewood in her hand proud that she had been given the responsibility. "How is the porridge cooking in your hut?", Njoroge asked. At once Wairimu knew what he meant and said "It is cooking well". "Alright, go and tell the others to wash and quickly prepare the horns."

As soon as the children had conveyed the message to the neighbours, one by one, with their wives dragging along behind, they reported their presence to Njoroge by shouting Christmas greetings. *"Thigukuu! Muthenya munene."*

Komu and Ndicu were still together. First they went where Komu had been sent; then to where Ndicu had been sent. Now in this latter home there was a boy of their own age who was so dirty that flies used to keep him company all the time: Gikuri they called him, the dirtiest of dirt. "I can come along as well", Gikuri announced and started dragging slowly along behind them. "Where do you think you're going?", Ndicu asked, turning to face his step-brother as if to ask for his approval. Gikuri said, "I am going to the party: I am an adult too." "Make sure that you don't come home", Komu warned. "Not with that dirt on you or I'll scrub you without water." "Okay, I'm just going my own way. Any law against my going where I please?", Gikuri enquired, trailing behind like a puppy. But he was quite sure that he would go to where the smell of the roasting meat was coming from. "You naughty, greedy rat, if I see you there, you can tell me whether you have been invited all right", Komu warned him again, and ran forward, whistling as if he was calling a dog, making gestures with his hand and snapping his fingers. There was no dog behind him, and Gikuri, who obviously knew what was meant by those signs, couldn't care less. At home everybody was waiting anxiously and preparing himself for the feast. Komu and Ndicu were the last children to arrive back: they had wasted lot of time arguing with Gikuri. "Come here, my son", the father called from the centre of the circle. "We have been waiting for you." Komu breathlessly led the way to the centre. And Ndicu, realising that the time had been waiting for had come, followed his brother, despite the fact that his father had not used the plural "Sons".

Njoroge lifted a calabash full of salted blood mixed with some sour milk and handed it to his son Komu. "Drink that, my son, even though you are disobedient sometimes." Komu took hold of the calabash and started drinking. Ndicu looked at his throat and, finding how fast it was moving, gave Komu a scratch on his knee. Komu looked around with a bloody mouth and saw Ndicu staring at him with pleading eyes which spoke louder than words and that seemed to say, "Have you forgotten me, brother?" So Komu unwillingly handed the calabash to his step-brother, after making sure that he had had enough of the stuff. Ndicu drank, and finding that he was not satisfied, started licking the calabash with his tongue.

Noon found Komu and his step-brother sweating after the hard work of gnawing the bones. Komu was putting the finishing touches to a foot-long piece of rib when Ndicu pinched him again. This time he was so annoyed that he almost hit Ndicu with the bone, but Ndicu was quick enough to deliver his message: he pointed somewhere and Komu irritably looked to where

he was pointing. His anger was doubled when he saw
someone, a man, give a piece of meat to the very Gikuri
he had warned off minutes ago. He saw Gikuri receive
the meat and run behind one of the huts. Anger burned
Komu fiercely and, without waiting, the two boys ran
after Gikuri with such circumspection and haste that
none noticed them and Gikuri had no chance of running
away.

Gikuri was about to sit down when he saw them
coming: they saw him too. "Hey", he gasped and took
to his heels. They followed him and the race gathered
momentum. After a short and serious race, Komu could
hardly see Gikuri. Instead he just saw a brown sheet
trailing in the air like a kite, and an object underneath
it making some gesture.

Ndicu was left behind: he had eaten more than
necessary and his stomach was making him quite un-
comfortable, so he gave up the race after finding his
tummy too heavy to drag along. Komu joined him.
"He's gone!", he said breathlessly. "I tell you that boy
knows how to throw his legs forward, believe me! He's
like an ostrich, but one of these days I'll get him."
The two boys walked lazily homewards; then Ndicu
said abruptly, "An ostrich doesn't put on a pair of shorts.
He's like me. I can run like him too. Why, I haven't
any shorts." "Shut up!", Komu yelled, "You've never
seen an ostrich. You've never tried on a pair of shorts.
You always say things that you're not sure of." Then
they kept quiet. As they neared Ndicu's hut, Ndicu
said, "I'm thirsty, let me drink some water." And then they
both went in. "Hey! It's still here!", Ndicu said. Komu
looked under the bed and saw the two heaps he had
seen earlier in the morning, and, on all fours, he crawled
under the bed. "I just want to make sure, that's all",
he said. Ndicu sat on his haunches and watched. He saw
him lift the lid and put his nose near the mouth of the
gourd. "Muh! Muh!", he heard him say, like a cat.
"Bring me a horn", Komu ordered. "There are no horns

here—they were taken to the party", Ndicu answered. "Okay, bring me that hosepipe. I only want to taste it." Ndicu threw him a four-foot hosepipe which was lying on the floor. Komu grabbed it, and, putting one end into the gourd, he held the other end to his mouth and glanced at Ndicu as if to say, "You won't tell father, will you?" And then he started sucking. "Hey!", Ndicu shouted and started dancing, "I'll go and report you if you won't let me . . . ." "Come here, you little fool. No, close the door first", Komu said angrily. Ndicu closed the door and on all fours he crawled under the bed too. "I'll start sucking", Komu said. "Count up to five and then I'll give you the pipe." Ndicu did not know how to count in English so he used his own language. "Okay, go! *Imwe, igiri, ithatu, inya, ithano.*" And with that, he grabbed the pipe and started sucking and, from Komu's expressions, he knew the liquor was bitter. "One, two, three, four, five." Komu counted in English so quickly that Ndicu only had a few gulps before unwillingly giving up the pipe. Komu had the pipe again and this time his eyes were quite red. They went on sucking without any worries. Komu was lying on his stomach, supporting his chest with his elbows. Ndicu was lying on his back with his knees high in the air. They were totally drunk. Ndicu was holding the pipe while Komu counted, "One, two, three, four—" and then he grabbed the pipe for himself. "Hey!", Ndicu shouted drunkenly, "Stop that rotten English of yours. You're deceiving me! I . . ." "Go away and eat ashes", Komu answered and started pulling at the pipe. But Ndicu would not let go. "I'll go and report you", Ndicu threatened. "That won't buy you anything: you're up to your neck in this business too", Komu replied. The two boys started quarrelling and then the quarrel developed into a fight: the more they shouted, the more they got drunk.

Meanwhile at the party, the guests, after they had eaten the meat, gathered together and started drinking,

Njoroge being the headman. He was holding the gourd in his lap and supplying liquor to the party with horns. Kuria was on his right. Everybody had emptied at least five horns each and from the look in their eyes they were obviously drunk. Among the guests there was one man, Njenga by name, whom Njoroge hated very much. His daughter had had an illegitimate child which was contrary to the law, and Njoroge resented this very deeply. Actually Njenga had not been invited but, following the aroma of the roasting meat from his home, he had been led here, and so he settled down like the rest of the guests. Unfortunately—or rather, fortunately—he had forgotten to call his wife. Njoroge gave him a hostile look, but dared not say a word.

They were all singing drunkenly with their eyes half closed. The men were boasting how brave they were: "Who am I?", Kuria, the ugly man, shouted. "I killed an *imuyu* which was devouring the sheep and goats, and which wouldn't let our children sleep at night! I killed it with just one blow from my spear! I am the greatest! Hey!" And then the women applauded to emphasise his words. Among the women was Komu's mother. For some minutes she had trouble with her conscience: it was a long argument as to whether she had heard a scream outside. And, finding that she could not concentrate on what the rest of the women were doing, she excused herself, as if she were going to relieve herself, and ran outside. Reaching the fresh air, Komu's mother heard more screams. She ran to where they were coming from, and entered the hut that contained the *njohi*. She jerked open the door and was shocked to find the two boys, under the bed, pulling the hosepipe away from each other, with the gourds rolling on the floor and spilling the *njohi* everywhere. At first they did not see her but when they finally saw her they crawled from under the bed, one after the other, guiltily. But when they tried to stand up, they couldn't: they were completely overcome by the wine.

She started tearing her clothes angrily; then thought better of it. She paced here and there, like one possessed; then she tried to lift one of the boys. It was then she lost her balance. She staggered about with the boy in her hands like a sack of beans, here, there and everywhere. Then abruptly they both fell to the ground like a heavy load of firewood. The boy winced a little at the pain. Quickly she covered his mouth with her hand and kept it there lest her husband should hear. They sat on the floor helplessly and, after a few minutes more, the boys started dozing. Hurriedly she managed to put them on the bed, being careful not to attract anyone's attention. On the bed, Komu started dreaming. "Go away and eat ashes, Ndicu", he shouted in his sleep, "I can't let you have this pipe . . . ." And then he slept soundly. Komu's mother ran back to the party before anyone discovered her absence. She was so frightened her husband might ask for some more wine that her knees were shaking.

Years before, when Njoroge was a young man, he had met a terrific disaster which had cost him his left leg. Fortunately, however, he had been left with his left thigh on which to put the gourd during the wine-drinking.

It was two years after he had married his third wife that he happened to find a girl-friend out of a clear blue sky.

Neither party took the affair seriously because she was already somebody's wife and they both knew it. But the owner of the property, or the husband, Njoroge never knew personally, and he never bothered to know him. As the days passed by, they found themselves meeting secretly in the dark. "What if he discovers us? You know how you men spy on your wives", Njoroge was asked one night, and he answered like a man, "I don't even know him, and if he does discover us, I'll be only too glad to get acquainted. And if he wants more than that, then I'll scrub him without water!"

So he comforted her and, like fools, they increased

their meetings: in secret and in darkness.

But then there is a saying in Njoroge's language that "a thief's days are numbered". Njoroge knew this and his conscience kept reminding him of it; but he sort of ignored it, by simply saying "I know a thief's days are numbered, and they are forty which means I've got ten to go! Still I don't see why I should call myself a thief since I'm just taking care of some property whose owner is too careless. That is all." But then his conscience would ask him, "Did the careless owner ask you to do it? Did the owner really ask you to milk his cow? Is he sick? And if he did ask you, then why don't you wait until morning? Suppose you knock the calabash over and spill the milk because of the darkness?" And then Njoroge, unable to answer these questions, would shrug his shoulders and scratch his head and say, "Well, if you mean to steal, do the business wholeheartedly. If you get away with it, then thank God. And if they catch you red-handed, then thank Satan and tell him to await you in his kingdom because you're on your way."

Njenga, after having called his wife twice from his hut without receiving any answer, said loudly to himself, "I'm supposed to whip her if I call a third time and don't get an answer. They're all the same, like untrained donkeys. If you don't use a whip for a few days, they forget it and what it tastes of, and then you're obliged to shout until your ear-drums ache with pain. You could keep on barking like a mad dog, and still they wouldn't hear you."

And with that, he started to go to her hut. "I'll use my hands this time, instead of the whip. She's so naughty." But when he reached it, there was no one inside. So he had to swallow his anger and call his next wife. He took it that she had gone to borrow some salt from the neighbours. "She's as lucky as a little flea which escapes after having bit you. But, ehe, when I do get hold of her, she'll tell me where her father has hidden his-bee-hives", he said irritably.

The next day, his wife was not there when he called again. Likewise on the third and fourth day, until he became suspicious that something was going on. So he decided to investigate, quietly and without notifying anyone. Two nights he tailed his wife but somehow she managed to give him the slip. And every night she was carrying a little gourd. Njenga knew the gourd as well as he knew his wife: it was the gourd in which his milk was put every day, and the sight of it made him more certain that there must be another Njenga existing somewhere, whose privileges were equal to his.

The fifth night found Njenga ready with his weapons, waiting for her to go out. "Eh, yes", he thought excitedly, as he saw her, carrying the little gourd, sneak behind the hut and away over the fence. "Well, let's go as well", Njenga thought. "At least we can do the introductions tonight."

Njenga followed behind quietly and she led the way to a little bush not far from home. "Ha!", he gasped, as he saw a broad-shouldered giant of a man hug his own wife lovingly. Njenga crawled along until he was able to hear their conversation clearly. "You're late. I thought you weren't coming", the man said, shaking the gourd and then drinking the milk. "We can't go on like this: my husband is missing me and I ... Oh!" She screamed as she saw Njoroge fall down instantly, with his left leg a long way away from him. Then she saw the sword on the ground and, as if chased by a mad dog, she ran away as fast as her shaking legs could carry her. Once in the village, she almost missed her hut because of the shock, and when she had located it, she jerked open the reed door, latched it after her and went to her hide bed to get back her breath. Then she remembered her husband's gourd in which she had carried milk to the bush. "Ngai! I forgot it! It's useless to deny that you've eaten some meat when you have blood all over your lips. I'm really in trouble. I ... I ... I'll have to admit it. That hyena! That stupid hyena and me, a stupid donkey . . . what a fool I am!"

"Eh . . . Oh . . . Eh . . . Lorr . . .!", sighed Njoroge, on the ground with agony, unable to stand up and get acquainted as he had planned. "Oh . . . Lord . . . Oh, mother I've lost my leg . . . that ugly bitch . . . ." Njenga was standing by his side, spear high in the air. "Yes you have, and I want to chop the other one off too, right now", Njenga said, vindictively and menacingly, "and that I'm sure will stop you from stealing your neighbour's wife." And he knelt down to reach for the other leg. "Oh . . . . Lord . . . Stop him . . . I . . . Oh, please let me explain . . . . I just . . ." "You can explain to everybody by the time I've finished with you", Njenga said. "Oh no. Please . . . please I can't face the public. I know I'm guilty. I . . . Look here, my man, you're a man like me. You're not an ugly donkey like your wife I . . . . Suppose I happen to meet you with one of my wives You know you can't help it. Let us talk like men. What do you want? I'll give you anything, even my wife, provided you don't kill me", Njoroge pleaded. And Njenga, finding that he could get rich so quickly and so easily, changed his mind and said, "Okay, my man, I am a man like you and I think I can forgive you. But I think you have to do something to keep my mouth shut . . . ." "Yes, yes, I'll give you forty goats . . . and . . . yes, all those", Njoroge promised. Njenga was a fast thinker. He accepted the offer at once, being quite sure that he had not killed the goose and that it would continue to lay him golden eggs. He rushed off and called his friends to come and help him carry Njoroge home. "It was a very big leopard", he lied to his friends. "It stole one of his goats and, believe me, this man would be top of the class if all fools were to be graded. He followed the animal alone. Fortunately I reached him in time, before its paws got to his throat. But his foolishness has cost him his leg. He deserved it." Njenga convinced his friends, and, turning to Njoroge, said, "You're not feeling any pain, my man, are you? No, I know you're not. You're brave, aren't you, wanting to get acquainted with the beast, eh? Wait until we reach home and then I'll put some hot fat on it. It will heal soon, believe me." Njoroge was groaning.

And so Njoroge lost his left leg and everybody—with the exception of Njenga and his wife—took it that a big leopard had robbed him of his leg while it was pursuing his goat. And Njenga never dared ask his wife about the little gourd for fear that she might ask him about the leg.

Soon after Njoroge's wound had healed and he had started using his crutches, Njenga approached him again and said, "I'm glad that we're acquainted after all. It's splendid to see that you have recovered but... I... well I think you've got to do something to keep my big mouth shut. Remember how you shut it the other time. I don't want much this time. I'm quite sympathetic and want to cooperate. Ten he-goats will do for the time being, then we'll discuss the future later." Njoroge all but shouted, "You cold-blooded donkey. You're a donkey like that wife of yours! I'll kill ...." Then he held his tongue: it was useless debating with an obstinate man like Njenga, and, from the smile on his face, Njoroge knew that he was really licked; they were playing a game and he was obviously the loser. So he had no alternative but to give the ten he-goats and get rid of this clever rabbit. And, as Njenga had remarked before, they would discuss the future later.

Njenga whistled softly as he led the goats away and, looking back at Njoroge who was standing near his cow-shed, said sarcastically, "I'll see you later, my dear friend. You know that a friend in need is a friend indeed. You're just the right man ... Eh ... No ... I might pay you another visit soon so that you can seal my lips properly. There's a leak in them somewhere, and I know you don't like that. I don't like it either. I'll try to visit you before we discuss the future."

But then fate was on Njoroge's side: before Njenga

could pay the visit, it was discovered that he had somebody's daughter pregnant. And, worst of all, the child
was illegitimate. Njenga was very annoyed and frightened
because he was sure that he would have to pay the penalty.
The penalty might be large or it might be reasonable,
nobody knew: it depended on the judge. It was all these
thoughts that occupied his mind and made him forget
about Njoroge. But when the day finally came, Njenga
was very shocked to find that there were five elders to
judge him with Njoroge trailing behind them, hopping
ponderously. And, from the way he was behaving,
Njenga knew at once that Njoroge was the leader of the
group. "Hey", he gasped to himself, "my head will be
shaved without water, I'm sure. The hyena will avenge
itself now: it will make me betray my father's beehives."
He made a sharp crack with his tongue and shook his
head with anger. Njoroge saw him and said, "There's
another army of elders coming along behind. It's not
only us. Make sure that you slaughter enough animals."
And Njenga said, demurely and so quietly that his voice
was inaudible, "Hm . . . hm . . .you think I'll slaughter
your mother's animals? It's your own animals I'm going
to kill . . . you fool."

Women brought stools and everybody sat down and
waited eagerly to hear Njoroge speak. Njoroge introduced
his group to the family and then continued with the
preliminary talks. Finally he said: "Our comrade's
she-goat's leg has been broken. By his carelessness.
However, the bees have been disturbed and are out of
the hive. You've got to pay twenty fat he-goats because
of the bees. Twenty he-goats to our warriors. And the
fattest ram you have to the honoured elders who spent
their time delivering this important message. And finally
you must pay the fine, twenty sheep, respectfully."
Njenga thought over that one bitterly and then abruptly
announced, "Go to hell. You . . . you . . . worthless . . .
fool!" "Ten more sheep as a fine for abusing the elders",
Njoroge announced pompously. Njenga thought bitterly

and then he remembered something: "He's really come to seal my lips as I advised him. What a devil he is! Wait until they've left and then I'll teach that bastard a lesson."

Njoroge with his elders left the place and after that day he didn't see Njenga again for a long time. Thus the reader will understand why Njoroge was so astonished to see Njenga come to his party, despite the fact that he had not been invited.

Komu's mother sat on her stool and tried to be as inconspicuous as possible. However, an old man who was sitting near her noticed her at once and handed her a hornful of wine. "Here", he said, "drink this. I know that once upon a time you were a beautiful she-goat, but age has cramped us. We are just like empty hives or old . . . old . . . cows which a lion won't even dare kill." She handed back the horn. The old man, who had lost his front upper teeth, was lisping so that you couldn't distinguish whether he was saying "she" or "se". He emitted a sharp blare into the air and everybody kept quiet. Then he sang: "Who is I? Eh? My first wife bore me three strong he-goats. The first he-goat encountered Masai warriors two months after his circumcision. They tossed him in the air, and, as he came tumbling through the air, they planted spears and he landed on them. The sharp weapons turned his intestines inside out and you know what happened next. The second he-goat eloped with his friend's girl-friend. The boy followed them because he was mad but I wouldn't dare tell you what he did to my son. My third he-goat went berserk. He met his mother as she was coming from the shamba with her basket on her back and he took her soul away.

"Then he approached me as I came from the cow-shed carrying a four-hour-old calf. He threw his spear at me. The weapon missed me and caught the poor creature. The animal went to sleep. He threw his club.

Unfortunately this one hit my mouth and threw me on the dust. I reached for my sword, and before the mad he-goat could finish me, I finished him first and got rid of the bad seed. In my mouth I felt some hard objects. I thought they were small stones and was not surprised to find that my upper gum was quite empty. Who among you has ever encountered such a mystery, eh? You only...." Another sharp cry echoed around the place and everybody turned to see Njenga—the uninvited guest—open his mouth and say: "Who is I? I have got all my teeth in my mouth. I married a wise wife. She deceived me with a giant of a man. And, believe me, she almost made me rich. The man lost his leg and his sheep and I'm still going to have...." "Shut your noise", Njoroge all but shouted. He stood up. Njenga went on with his song. "People happen to betray themselves.... I was just....", but before he could finish, Njoroge seized a stool and, throwing it in the air with some force, lost his balance. A big gourd which had been put on a stool stopped him as he came hopping helplessly. The big gourd dropped to the ground with a bang, and burst. The wine in it splashed, and before he knew, Kuria, the ugly man, found himself all drenched with wine.

The stool went up like a bullet and caught Njenga's forehead, knocking him unconscious. The women started scratching their heads and screaming fearfully. Njoroge was mad with rage. He took one good hop and reached a flaming piece of firewood from the kitchen. He swung it, but before he could throw it, Kuria caught it in the air. A voice shouted, "Let him throw it and kill the dog. He laughed at me because of my empty gums! Let...." Njoroge emitted a sharp cry, "Let me kill him. Let me. He's a donkey like his nasty wife. Let me...." Kuria seized him, together with his crutches, put him over his shoulder and took him to his hut, latching the door on him.

And everybody, even the smallest child, knew that the

Christmas party was over: there and then. Some moaning, some crying loudly, some laughing, the children crying and the dogs barking; the guests left the place with great commotion.

Komu slept soundly, unaware that his father was fighting. When he awoke it was dark and he was so dizzy and had such a headache. It was only after long thinking that he realised what had happened. He started crawling from the bed, then he saw his companion sleeping soundly, knees high in the air. "Phew, he's a sound sleeper", Komu thought. He unlatched the door and walked out. His knees were weak and, judging from what he was feeling, he was not yet sober. His head was going round as if he had sniffed a pinch of snuff. He was trying to locate his mother's hut when suddenly he caught sight of a fire under the fig tree. At once he remembered that his father must be there with the rest of the boys. So he changed his mind and decided to join the group. But when he reached there, he saw only his father, alone with a little gourd beside him. "Go and bring me a horn quickly", the father ordered. But before Komu had left, his mother came with a horn. She gave Komu a very curious look which conveyed some accusation. "Where did you . . . ?", she started, and then kept quiet because her husband was near, and quickly she dashed away. Njoroge sipped the *njohi* slowly and with great concentration. Komu kept quiet: he was thinking about his school, his classmates, and his teachers. One teacher was white—Rev. Brown. He was teaching them many things about religion, and of course they used to listen with a great deal of attention. Yes, he had taught them something about Christmas too. Yes, he had explained quite clearly the meaning of Christmas. But why didn't he say anything about Komu having been born at Christmas? "Father", Komu said, "what is this Christmas? What do you really mean by Christmas?" His father all but scolded him. "You little brat, don't you know that that was when I married your mother?"

Komu squirmed uncomfortably, and, finding that his question had not been answered satisfactorily, he resumed his former manner and kept quiet. The father gave the question a second thought. He knew that he had lied to his son, but that was the only answer which had come to mind. "What a bad day", he thought bitterly, and started to go through it, right from the beginning when he had been wakened by his son in the morning. Yes, and the faithful son had greeted his father. "Then I sent him to call my wives, and when he came back, I was mad and wanted to fix him so early in the day. But what made me mad I don't know. Yes and then the animal wanted to revenge itself because I had castrated it. Yes, the beast broke my crutch and threw me in the dust in front of my wives and children." Njoroge made a sharp crack with his tongue and shook his head angrily; then he went back to his thoughts. "But everything went all right from then, until this devil showed up. Oh, he really made me sick! And after his arrival, everything went zigzag. Yes, really zigzag, for he reminded me of that mysterious night when he chopped my leg off. Yes, and then he started blackmailing me. The devil he did! And, in spite of all that, he came to boast in front of my guests and my wives. Yes, then I went and sealed his lips with a stool. Yes, he deserved it. I did not intend to cause any embarrassment today; just the opposite in fact. And to make it worse, this brat here asked a question that you wouldn't have thought him capable of, with all that innocence of his. But . . . oh . . . poor kid . . . my poor son. I've lied to him for the first time. Oh Lord! Christmas! Christmas! Christmas was there even before I had thought of marrying my wife. Christmas . . . a foreign story which I, of course, cannot explain to my son. What could I tell him Christmas is ? It is not really his birthday. But then I cannot remember the day when he was really born. Eh, to hell with Christmas. What is all this ? Some bad witch must have . . . ."

"Father", Komu interposed, and because he was

not yet sober, he was apparently quite bold. "What
is . . . well . . . I . . . we were looking after the cattle
one day and a hyena whose hind leg was broken tried
to hop past us, but it was killed later. And believe me
that animal was hopping like mad. I . . . well . . . why
do *you* hop like . . . well . . . where did your leg go,
father?" The father jerked back, as though the voice
had struck him with the impact of a physical blow.
Some glittering beads of cold sweat started to show on his
forehead. Then, automatically, he said, "A big leopard
stole my leg, my son." Then he tightened his lips.
Komu tried to look into his eyes, but every time the
father avoided his little eyes. His face showed that he
was labouring under great strain. He knew that he had
lied to his beloved son for the second time. "But what
other answer could I have given him?", he thought
bitterly. "He is too young to know the real story. What an
unlucky day it is!" He cursed, then he looked up and
saw the little gazing eyes. "Komu, my son", he said.
"Come here and stay with your old father." Komu
crawled over and threw himself beside his father. Njoroge
patted his son lovingly, and, stroking his small head
tenderly, said, "Everybody seems to have run away
from me today, my son. You were quite brave to come
and keep your father company. But he has lied to you
twice today." "How? How, father?", the son asked
curiously, but, looking up into his father's eyes, he got
the answer: his big father's eyes were half closed with
some sparkling tears which were now streaming over
his cheeks. Komu took a deep, bated breath and, finding
that he could fight them no longer, let his hot tears stream
over his little cheeks; automatically he shared his father's
grief. Suddenly the father jerked, as if bitten by a flea.
"Yes", he announced, "Yes, you know the answer
now." "My son", he said, with courage. "You greeted
me this morning. Did I answer your greeting?" Komu,
with tearful eyes, looked up apprehensively and said,
"No, father, you did not." The father smiled. He had

found the answer to his problem. But the son kept quiet
with confusion.

Back home

He was jumping up and down happily, like a busy mother weaver-bird flapping her wings and squeaking and whistling in the morning, in order to wake her children up for the day ahead.

He whistled softly and hummed a song they had been taught recently by one of the Peace Corps in his school.

He had been happy before, but now that he had done all the work there was to be done, his happiness increased all the more. His heart drummed inside him and his head was full of sweet music; and his body was warm and vigorous. This was happiness and he was feeling it inside him.

And now, as he strode across Kilombero Street to a little shop on the other side, the joy burned inside him like coal, as he remembered the sharp glance Jane had cast on him when she had come to say goodbye to him after the formal, end-of-term ceremony.

Now that they had parted, now that she was not near, he longed for her. It was true that Jane had taken his fancy. And as he looked at the whole affair more intently, he wondered whether really she had not fallen in love with him. For example, that look—that penetrating, shy look she always gave him when he was not looking at her. But because he had never fallen in love before, because he was new to the world of lovers, he suddenly found himself trying to find answers to certain questions. Questions he had never thought of before, questions such as: "What's it like to fall in love? Is falling in love something tangible? Does one know that one has fallen in love?" And other questions harder than these; more unanswerable, baffling, and headache-giving queries. They excited him; they intoxicated him. And now as he was crossing the road, his head pregnant with such questions, a passing car almost ran over him. He jumped off the road in time. And his head was pregnant no more: the emergency had dismissed Jane from his mind for the moment.

He entered the little, dirty, hidden shop at the corner, which harboured a considerable amount of stench. The owner, who was as dirty and filthy as his commodities, welcomed him cordially and greeted the boy in his own language. His eyes sparkled with joy; happiness took hold of him again and instead of answering the greetings in the usual way, he gesticulated, furiously and confusedly. The good and sweet words he wanted to say stuck in his mouth and were swallowed by excitement—never ever to come out. He was so happy to listen to his language again after a long, dreadful period of speaking English and Swahili in school.

Later he bought a calico sheet which was dyed red and designed specifically for Masai. Unless he was a Masai, no man would dream of touching the calico sheet, let alone buying it. They had a deadening smell, an unearthly stench which, if you were not familiar with it, could give you a headache: to a Westerner, the smell was a blow strong enough to confine him to a hospital bed. Yet to a real, typical Masai, it was the sweetest perfume in his nostrils. When the boy bought it, he knew its purpose, he knew its worth. And now that he had received his money's worth, his body was warm with joy and his heart thumped inside him, rhythmically and tremendously so that he listened and heard it: "Boum, boum, boum."

The boy's name was Ole Msanga and he was a Masai.

Who could tell how long his happiness would last?
Who knew that his happiness would turn completely into sadness?

Who could tell that the boy would be crying instead of
   laughing?
Ole Msanga was a student at one of the schools in
Arusha and now that the school had closed he was preparing to go and see his parents back home.
He was the result of the union of Msanga and Nduta
who had, as it were, made a very uncongenial couple.
Msanga was over fifty while his wife was in her twenties.
It always happened that whenever one of them wanted
this, the other wanted that: they never wanted the same
thing at the same time. Even though she had succeeded
in keeping their disagreements away from the eyes of
the other wives, Nduta always wondered what caused
them. And because she had been kidnapped when she
was ten when the Masai won the battle against the Kikuyu,
she had a feeling that the Kikuyu gods were probably
annoyed with her because she had agreed (though, in
fact, she hadn't) to be married to Ole Msanga, a Masai—
her own people's greatest and most implacable enemy.
And so the gods had decided to castigate her by imposing
such strong disagreements between her and her husband.
So strong was this feeling in her that it had made her
believe that it had only been by chance that their union
that night had resulted in Ole Msanga. She was so
confident because, apart from Ole Msanga, they had no
children. The other wives had children of course. Lots
of them. But she had only one. She had only Ole Msanga.
Not that she was less fertile than the others; not that
Msanga's power had been carried away by the years;
not that they never came to each other again. No:
simply because the disagreements between them were
always interfering with their life. Msanga was rich and
had many wives, so it was no wonder that he cared
comparatively little about Nduta, even though she was
young. The only alternative was to have children by
another man, but this she found too great a risk to take:
there was her social life to care about. Why it would
make the greatest scandal if she had a child who, instead

of resembling Msanga, looked like another man—and probably a well-known man in the society at that. And ... and ... anyway, fate knew what would happen to her if that occurred.

Ole Msanga woke up early next morning. A journey of more than thirty miles lay ahead of him. He unfolded his new, red, filthy calico and admired it. Then he gracefully and carefully folded it and put it on a kerchief which was spread on the floor. Beside it he put another little bundle and then tied the ends together, tightly and yet carefully. He gazed vacantly at the room and then satisfied, he left and showed the door his back.

Two days ago the students had been laughing their heads off at his traditionally-holed ears and his two, missing, lower front teeth which prevented him pronouncing his "s" distinctly. He had made them laugh all the more by telling them that these two teeth were traditionally plucked out early in the morning, before breakfast. Well if they knew that he was going back to Masailand; if they knew that he was going to herd cattle; if they knew, above all, that he wouldn't wear a pair of shorts for the whole of the holiday and would just have the red calico sheet wrapped around him—they would probably laugh their guts out. On the other hand, he thought, if Jane met him without a pair of shorts, she would probably look at him no more. She wouldn't understand. Only a Masai would understand. Anyway, he wouldn't abandon his cultural traditions just because of nonsensical words and laughter from the students. Or from anybody. They could go to hell as far as he was concerned.

He walked majestically along an isolated path, feeling happy and free. He hummed again and whispered the sweet song he loved. Again the mother weaver-birds responded and whispered and squeaked at the tops of their voices in their nests on top of the trees. Both songs filled the atmosphere with pleasant music. And the atmosphere responded in its turn and kept calm and swallowed the music: not too cold and not too warm. And the heavens, hating to be the exception, responded too and exhaled peace and glory. And they whispered and whistled and hummed and squeaked, again and again and again.

The town came and went. The suburbs came and went. And later the crooked huts, which seemed to totter as he passed them, invited him challengingly; then showed him their bare backs; then slowly they were all swallowed up by the distance. And he saw them, he saw the town, he saw the suburbs, no more.

On and on he hiked. The sun stood proudly in the sky like a king. Or like a Masai hero. Nobody had the guts to rebuke it. Nobody had the power to conquer it. It was there, whether you liked it or not. And it was a part of life. It was both advantageous and disadvantageous to him. It made him saturated with sweat, and it imperceptibly stole some of his courage. But with it shining in the sky, he knew what time it was, and without it in this great sea of wilderness, he would have been blind. Blind in both his eyes and in his sense.

Soon he approached Masailand. Homeland.

Not that there was a boundary; not that anybody had pointed it out to him before: but a sudden instinct made him believe that he was in Masailand. And now that he was in Masailand, he had better adapt himself to the Masai way of life. He sat down under an umbrella-like tree and undid his shirt; took his shorts off; took his shoes off and took off his underwear. Now that he was in the nude, he felt fresh and free and active. This moved him so much that it reminded him of the day when his parents had almost denied their love for him:

His father had been talking to another man, with a calabash full of milk in his hands, when Ole Msanga came and sat down beside him. Suddenly his father stopped talking and threw his nose in the air. This was abruptly followed by a hard slap on Ole Msanga's shoulder; and then a long string of obscenities followed, unceremoniously. "Away with you at once!", the father roared. "Away with you, brat! You have fouled the air, you little devil! Can't you sit down on your two buttocks? Eh? I knew what was going to happen when I saw you sitting on one buttock. I knew. How many times have I told you to behave? Take your buttocks to your mother and tell her to check if they've got jiggers in them. At once. Before I go mad and curse you."

Ole Msanga left with a heavy heart. He knew for sure that he really had not fouled the air. If not the other man then it was his father who had done it, and because of shame he had decided to make his son the culprit. This was not the first time: Msanga had done it several times before. Sometimes it made a loud noise. When this had happened, he had coughed or groaned or done something to distract his son's attention. Then he would chase him away: he wouldn't admit to his son that he himself had fouled the air.

When, however, Ole Msanga, as he had been instructed, took his buttocks to his mother, she was far from affectionate: she rebuked him and reproached him angrily. "Go out and mix with the other men, you little fool! Why do you like sitting around with women? They foul the air and say all sorts of things! You'll become a noodle. A fool like Ole Tipis. Now get out before we foul the air in front of you. Go, go . . . ."

Ole Msanga, like an outcast or like a degraded Masai warrior, walked out slowly, full of sorrow, and sat under an umbrella-like tree. The thought of Ole Tipis took charge of him:

Ole Tipis was a boy more like a skeleton than a human. His thin body and bones, which were vaguely blanketed by a thin, filthy, oily skin, were far from attractive to the eyes. The stick-like, long, thin legs were fixed underneath the body and buckled and collided as he walked. His ghostly, long and bony arms, which seemed to be coming off as he swung them, were ambiguously attached to either shoulder. On the top was, dubiously, placed a pumpkin-like head which he, unable to balance it properly, allowed to lean on one shoulder. The belly protruded forward like a pregnant woman's and yet it was crammed with nothing but foul air and long, sick entrails which coiled and twisted inside, hand in hand with tape-worms which did their business alternately with hook- and round-worms. They said that he was made of the worst clay, the leavings after God had finished his work. He was an outcast in the society, yet they accepted him because he gave them something to talk about, something to laugh at, to jeer at and to taunt. One day some boys decided to amuse themselves with him. They collected a big heap of newly-dropped cow-dung and covered it with some soil on top so that it was just concealed. Then they planted a blade of grass on the summit and started to compete to see who could pluck off the grass-blade with his bare teeth. They did this purposely, to attract Ole Tipis' attention. When, however, the boy came along and announced his desire to try, they respectfully gave way and allowed him to try—with mockery and laughter fixed on their faces. Ole Tipis knelt down importantly and straightened his ever-bent pate. Due to his strong confidence of winning he took his time and did every action slowly and importantly, just to let their anxiety and curiosity mature. With hands supporting him on the ground, he drew his ever-gaped mouth downwards towards the falsely-planted grass-blade on the covered cow-dung. The spectators held their breath and waited enthusiastically. When the foolish Ole Tipis was about to put his teeth on the grass, all the boys at once pressed his head downwards with such force that he couldn't resist. Then they let him free and ran away, laughing and gesticulating to each other happily, only to come back later to laugh much more strongly at the poor boy whose whole mouth was crammed with cow-dung. News of this trick was passed on from boy to boy and produced great laughter among them.

And now Ole Msanga's mother had told him that he would be foolish like Ole Tipis. It was a great insult to him. It was the worst insult to his status as a boy. However this incident had gone out of his mind, he had not known how, and he had found himself chatting and laughing as before.

Wonderful creatures children, he thought, as the fresh, cool, Masai air—which smelt of cows—beat against his naked body and awoke him from his reverie.

He untied his bundle and gazed at it admiringly. Then he took the red calico sheet and professionally, traditionally, wrapped it around his body. The Masai-made sandals, whose sole was the hide of a bull, took the place of the leather shoes which didn't belong here and therefore were unusable. His head was treated with some red substance which turned his soot-black hair blood-red. The holes in his ears were immediately plugged with well-cut, short, smooth pieces of sticks. After putting bangles where they belong—on the arms and legs—he folded the town clothes together and they gradually took the place of the Masai clothes in the kerchief.

And now that he was here he must eat Masai food as well. So he unfolded a piece of paper and, one by one, one after the other, the pieces of roasted meat saw their way from the paper via his hand, through his mouth and into his belly. This is the Masai way of eating: one piece of meat follows the other like the droppings of a goat, without leaving much time for mastication. This is the fashion. And they like it this way. If a Masai didn't know how to eat this way, then it would be no surprise if sometimes he didn't get anything to eat at all.

He realised that he hadn't forgotten it after the town's soft *ugali* which makes one's throat contract.

Now that he was full, now that he was a Masai, he started his journey to the north again.

The Masai had been blessed, he thought. All this land, all this rich pasture belongs to the Masai. It is theirs. Together with all the cattle. All the cattle belong to them. They were given all this fortune because they didn't know how to till the land. They can't bend their waists— their waists are inflexible. And their hands can't hold the *jembe*—they don't know how to. But a spear, a *simi*, is another matter. These are the tools which belong to the Masai, tools they can use without any difficulty at all. And that's why every other tribe is envious. The envy in these tribes is like ever-burning hell-fire. It is hereditary. Generation after generation inherit this from their fore fathers and fore mothers. And so every new generation is brought up to be virulent and to fight the Masai—to deprive them of their rights and to dominate them. "But who are the Masai anyway?" He emitted a sharp blare, heroically, in the air and then went all batty. He gesticulated furiously and imprecated and cursed and reviled disgustedly his tribe's enemies. The Masai-blood was circulating in his veins now. He vowed to himself and promised to fight his enemies until the Masai blood had dried in his veins. But what . . . what about Jane? Wasn't she an enemy? She wasn't a Masai actually. She was an Msukuma. Well, what about her and her people? Good Lord! How could he bear a grudge towards everybody, automatically, like that? What a bloody fool he was! Yes, but what about her then? To which part of his world did she belong? In which group was he putting her? "Damn it", he cursed, with confusion. "Well, as far as my tribe and culture are concerned, Jane can go . . . ." Go where? To hell? "No, never. I didn't want to put it that way . . . I . . . well . . . I don't know what . . . Good heavens, am I going out of my senses? What kinds of thoughts am I thinking? Don't I have anything better to think of? To hell with it all . . . ."

The more he thought about his tribe, the more he regained the courage to hike on. And hike he did . . . On and on, without tiring, without fear, without hunger or thirst, without a glimpse of a living soul; influenced and inspired by the thought of seeing his parents again, and the virulent hatred against his enemies, he boldly negotiated the invisible bitter waters of the unyielding wilderness like a solitary ship on the salty and coarse sea. Every now and then he ululated heroically. Every now and then he sang. Songs of war; songs of peace and happiness; and songs to praise his mother and father. Songs which revived the old memories of childhood; songs which conveyed his regret for being born alone. Sometimes he laughed loudly, other times he went into a fit and cried solitarily. But he never felt tired; never felt hungry at all . . . .

When the sun acquires its beautiful golden colours; when the sun slowly walks homewards, it is the harbinger of night.

As soon as the sun had walked out on him, the solitude and its effects reigned over his whole body tyrannically. the gusts of cold, evening air cut through his bare skin. He shivered a shiver which was a compound of cold, hunger, thirst and tiredness; fear and loneliness.

When the sun had been bloodlessly dethroned by the moon, the jackals and the hyenas began to call each other happily. This was *their* time now, and they were preparing to take advantage of it. As soon as the daylight was gone, the twilight as well came and went and gave way to the moon. And the moon majestically established her queenhood at once. And the whole world saw and accepted her glorious bright light, courteously.

Then, all of a sudden, the moon was deprived of her queenhood: the heavens cracked and then thundered heavily. Then dark darkness ensued and obscured the moon and her light and then swallowed them all into the cold belly of heaven. Then, as if the heaven and earth were kissing, all went quiet; the jackals and the hyenas kept mum and the world held its breath . . . and then slowly, like tear drops, the rain drops began gradually to fall. And it is at this time that people say "the Creator in heaven is pissing". And he went on pissing . . . pissing . . . until the animals—everything—were thoroughly saturated with "His urine".

The rain drops fell relentlessly from heaven like bullets. On his body they caused pain, but he dared not so much as put on his shirt. He was a young Masai who is entitled only to his calico sheet. It was a terrible fight between his body and his spirit. But the spirit was growing weaker and weaker, and the body won the fight in the end. And so he gave up and said, "To hell with the traditional culture", and then put on his shirt.

Suddenly, his body acquired that which made him tremble like a child. He was never at peace, any more. He was never brave again. Courage and boldness, like the sun, had suddenly deserted him. He shivered. His jaws clenched and his teeth knocked against each other. Then something put him on the alert and, slowly, he began to realise how vulnerable one is in Masailand. One is always amidst one's enemies wherever one is and whatever one is doing. There is the King of the Jungle who is never appeased. There are those greedy, fierce hyenas and jackals which can eat you up before you are quite dead. There are dangerous elephants and rhinos and buffaloes which will hardly let you pass without a "pat". Far to his north live the fierce, implacable Kuria people with their ever-sharp weapons; to his south are the Wamang'ati people—the bitterest Masai enemies; on the other sides are those merciless, insatiable Kikuyu and Wakamba of Kenya, who take the fight against the Masai as a part of their life. All these and others victimise the Masai. And now that he was wearing a shirt and it was dark, he could easily fall a victim to the Moran who would take him for a spy on their cattle. But God is merciful and, as they put it, "He neither eats cake nor drinks champagne": He remains unbribable for ever and ever.

He mercifully let the rain fall and so it kept all the

uncountable enemies at bay.

As the rain fell rhythmically, peace and darkness reigned over Masailand. The boy, in the heat of darkness and the cold of the rain, went—he didn't know where. At times he thought he was where his home had once been, but now it was there no more: there was neither the sign nor the smell of a human being. On and on he hiked in the dark womb of the jungle, but he never found his home. From his eyes two lines of tears came and mixed with the rain; in his mouth they had a disagreeable taste. Then, suddenly, he landed on something slippery. His tired knees thumped against each other, then against a rock, and then gave way. He tripped and then lost his balance and plunged into a thorny bush. He squealed painfully, but it was like the voice of John in the wilderness. He lay still, pinned there, and in his mind he saw Death with her bony knuckles beckon him with a smile on her face. He wouldn't go. Oh no. He plucked up some courage and with one jerk set himself free. Then, far far away, his dull eyes picked up a distant, faint, flickering light on the horizon. Whatever it was, it gave him courage: it seemed to call to him, "Come . . . come . . . come". And off he lumbered, and limped towards the distant light on the horizon.

It seemed as if a century—two centuries—had already elapsed before he finally came near the beckoning light. Yes, it came from a hut—a Masai hut obviously. The bright little light, which was borne on the hot flames of the warm, smouldering fire, invited him in; but, as a Masai, he knew better than to walk in on another Masai, carelessly. They are always capable of reminding one of one's manners with a blow from a good club.

At a reasonable distance, he conveyed his inquiries and needs in the form of a song. In the song, he pleadingly put all his calamities and entreated help. And then, with a hoarse voice, he terminated the begging song, due to the bitter sobs which intervened, helplessly.

The song must have been duly heard because a sort of

reed-door, whose fragments were oddly, clumsily integrated with hide strings, opened a crack and a voice came from inside. "Where are you going? Come here if you dare; I am ready with tools and it won't take long to deprive you of your life. Now come, if you have the guts." The boy heard all these words in pain. He knew quite well that the man was taking him for an enemy. But, in spite of all that, he felt secure, peaceful, now that he was near a human being: a man of his own tribe; a Masai, though unidentified. He forgot the calamities he had undergone, the danger in which he was, and the pains he had suffered. The appetite to speak to someone, to seek assurance, sympathy and pity overcame him and despite the heralded danger he suddenly had enough guts to go forward to meet his new enemy-friend, and to narrate his misadventures. Again in the form of a song, he told of what had befallen him while, at the same time, he advanced towards the hut. He sang in an appealing voice and begged for mercy:

"Here I come forward, father,
To meet your sharp weapons with my bare hands.
I throw myself on your wishes, old father.
If you want to skin me alive;
If you want to deprive me of my precious life;
It is just as you think best.
But here I come, bare-handed,
Neither an enemy nor a relative,
But a poor, poor boy in the heart of the wilderness
Who is more dead than alive."

"Now kill me if you have the guts yourself", he said pleadingly. He limped and limped again, and then collapsed at the door. Meanwhile, the old man was listening to the song, fascinated, with his bony hands clinging helplessly to his weapons.

Naturally moved, he went and dragged the collapsing boy inside and then fastened the fragmented door. Gradually he generously applied all the hospitality he could to the boy: blew the fire and added some more firewood; applied the sheep-tail oil to the whole body and wounds of the boy; and then, taking one hide and a piece of filthy old blanket from his bed on the floor, he made a comfortable bed on the floor near the sheep (but not near the goats) for his casual, unexpected guest. Sleeping near the sheep is warmer, more comfortable and peaceful than sleeping beside the goats: when the old man did this, he was demonstrating his utmost concern for the poor boy.

On the comfortable bed, near the green-eyed sheep, with a calabashful of goat milk in his hands and a big piece of roasted meat in another calabash on the floor, Ole Msanga felt secure and peaceful. He felt his courage come back to him. As, step by step, he told his story to the old, kind Masai, the former could hardly control his tears. When, however, he had finished and kept quiet, the old man kept quiet as well and continued to stare at him with his goatish eyes as if he was expecting some more story. Stillness ensued as the two people continued to stare at each other. The old Masai kept mum and spoke with his eyes: not smiling and not frowning; neither corrugating his well-worn-by-age face. Was he wholly moved by the story? Was he dubious? Was he suspicious? No, nobody could make it out. The answer was concealed by the goatish beard which made him revered, quite apart from his age. He did not so much as move his eyes from the boy. The boy stopped eating and was actuated by the fear that the old man might be a ghost, a spirit or a god—a Masai god or something. Then he jerked with a start as the old man cleared his voice. He cleared it again and threw the spittle into the fire.

"You are a fool", he said, looking into the boy's eyes, with a matter-of-fact voice. "You are a noodle. All of you who go and live in the town are bloody fools; foolish fools, if you know what I mean." Then he kept quiet and the effect of his words worked on the boy, as he had intended.

"Listen, my son. This thing you call 'town' is a great hypocrite. It is like a wise rat which gnaws at your heel and then blows on it to stop the pain. It teaches you the so-called 'modern ways of life' thoroughly well. On the other hand, it teaches you, very thoroughly, to abandon your old, old way of life—your culture. I say 'your culture' because you are young and you are taking over from me—I am old now and I don't mind any culture now, old or new. You are learning new and strange things now and you are ignoring, if not forgetting, the old and important things. I might be incomprehensible because I speak in riddles, but what I mean is this. You know very well that we Masai are not confined to one permanent place like other tribes; we don't stick to one particular place. We keep on migrating from one place to another, according to the pasture. When you left your so-called 'town', you knew this, but you deliberately ignored it because you are too obsessed with these modern town ideas. So you see what has become of you. You have been hungry and thirsty all day long; you have been walking like a spirit or a god-messenger; you have been wounded, drenched and, worst of all, you haven't—and it will take time—seen your parents.

"All my cattle, wives and children have already left and tomorrow I shall be following them with these sheep and goats. This place, besides being badly pastured, is quite insecure. The Sukuma people have recently learnt how to fight and how to steal our cattle.

"So it's only me who is left here. Tomorrow, before the sun wakes up, I'll be on my way. So, my dear son, why don't you make up your mind and come with me? You are tired. Go to sleep, but make up your mind before it is too late. Tomorrow either we go hand in hand, or we go separately like mad zebras."

"I shall come with you", the boy announced automatically, in an unnatural voice: just to please the old man perhaps; or perhaps the words escaped his mouth unawares. But later on, he regretted the rashness of his tongue.

The thing he was trying hard not to admit, the facts he had been effortly evading all along were now in the open: whether he admitted it to himself or not, his parents *had* migrated with the others. There was no alternative but to either go after them, to go with the god-like old man, or to march back to the comfortable, cosy and peaceful town. There was no third choice. His eyes automatically were wet—wet with hot, scalding tears. The sheep nearest him nuzzled against him and then started to chew the cud. The rhythmic chewing, the warmth from the woolly bodies, and the heavy breathing of the sheep were more of a lullaby and were sweeter in his head than the songs by which his mother had sung him to sleep in his childhood days. But before he lapsed into a sound sleep, Jane came into his mind again. And this time he saw her clearly, vividly as his saviour—a true, devoted saviour who was determined to save him. Everybody, his parents, his friends, even the whole tribe, seemed to desert him suddenly. Everybody was running away from him. He was a friendless, homeless boy. In this view, he saw Jane as his sister, his brother and finally as his love. Why, Jane was the only one who showed him any love: the others showed only hatred, mockery. Jane lived in another world, a different world from his. And suppose, just suppose, he joined her in her world and completely forgot his hideous, dreadful, retrogressive world—that peaceless, rough world! It was only Jane who could save him from himself. Just suppose he devoted more attention to her—suppose he cared for her and . . . for ever as well? Suppose they lived together for ever? What then? Things would undoubtedly be different: things would be good. Jane would give him love—everything he wanted —and this would blind him, would make him forget about everything. Everything, even his reactionary old culture. Why had he been such a fool—so great a fool, in fact, as not to respond to her charms more and more strongly? This was a lucky revelation indeed! He warmed up with happiness. He blamed himself for everything and longed terribly for the day he would see Jane again. The affair between Jane and him came to him in full force: it got the better of him so much that he forgot everything for a moment. In this light, he saw Jane in her true colours. He saw her as a true saviour. Ever since that conversation with the old man had taken place, he had been utterly confused. He didn't know where he was; didn't know to which world he belonged: either the Masai world or the town world. He had experienced a sensation—a peculiar sensation he would never forget. But the next minute Jane comes into the picture, right on cue, in his hardest hour.

"Yes, Jane, I knew you would come. Now look, Jane, we will school together until the day will come when we will be as inseparable as finger and ring. And together, you and me, we shall found and build a home—fancy, Jane, a home of our own!"

"Okay, my son, the time has now come for us to start our journey. I have put some sour milk in that gourd for you. We have a long, tiring journey before us, so we had better start off soon."

The darkness was slowly melting into twilight. The cold morning air cut into their skins like a knife. The old man coughed clumsily, self-consciously, and turned to look at the boy, who was as quiet as death. Their eyes met. The old man was taken aback. The antagonism, the hostility he saw in the boy's eyes spoke distinctly for itself. He uttered no word; nobody spoke. Slowly, the old man started to drive his sheep out of the hut for the journey. The sheep willingly picked the path and preceded him. When all was over, the old man, unwillingly yet incvitably, turned and looked at the boy.

"Go on, man. Go on with your journey and thank

you for everything; for all your hospitality."

"You are not coming?"

"Never"

"Never?"

"No, never."

Ole Msanga watched until the old man was gradually swallowed by the distance.

"Ah", he sighed with concentration. "Those Masai will never improve", he thought to himself moodily.

F. N. BARASA

Things take the wrong course

Slowly, hesitatingly, with much difficulty, he managed to lift his head an inch from where, almost like a pumpkin, it lay. It was evident that he was feeling pain as he went through this process of trying to lift his head off the hide bed. Every time he lifted it a quarter of an inch, he closed his weak eyes and contorted his already badly-wrinkled countenance into a form which clearly told of the strain he was undergoing more loudly than any words he could have spoken. This gesture was accompanied with a sigh so heavy that you might mistake it for the sigh uttered by a woman in childbirth. Yet, after tasting all these pains, after feeling their sting, he still would not give up; he wouldn't call the whole thing off and try to forget it all. Instead it seemed as though he was gathering courage with every passing minute.

Now the head was half a foot off the hide bed. "Eh . . . eh . . ."—another two inches—"Eh . . . eh . . . heee . . ." Now he was resting his bare chest and his head on his elbows. And now that he had got this far, it occurred to him that he needed a rest before he continued with this nerve-straining task of lifting himself off the bed.

In that position, then, he rested and let out a heavy "Whooooeeee" as if he had already performed a most important ritual. And then his eyes, so weak, so sunk in their withered sockets, opened a very little, as if they felt ashamed of opening at once. And this brought a considerable change in everything. Had this not happened indeed, things would have taken a different course; but fate had its way. No sooner had he opened his eyes than he saw her standing there like, like—and this was the best way he could put it—like a sacred tree, so unconcerned, so aloof, as if she didn't have a woman's heart at all. "You . . . ." The disgust, the wrath which was dominating him now filled his mouth, blocking the words with which he wanted to lash her. Instead he twisted his head slowly, involuntarily, giving her such a look as would have sliced her into nothingness, if it had been a knife. It sent jingles into her head, making her back shudder with fear. Involuntarily, helplessly, she took a step or two, undecidedly, forward. He was staring into space with disgust, cursing under his breath, trying to master his anger as much as possible.

Like a spider with a fly, he waited until she was near him. Then, just to please his fancy, he decided to give her the chance of lifting him into a sitting position. He was sure she would do exactly that. When this was done, he decided it would be time he acted, time he showed that, although he was old—too old now—although he was always sick, he was still the lord and master of everything in his household, be it a cat, a dog or a chicken let alone his wives. "Ah", he sighed, trying hard to hide the disgust in his voice. "Gaciku", he called, modulating his tone and burning like hell with the anger inside him. "Yũũũũ!", she answered, unaware of what was coming next. "Pass me my crook; I want to scratch my back." She was used to this kind of commanding and bossing: she passed the crook to her husband. The whole business was very natural; a day-to-day action, an action which was being performed by force of habit. But the business was only natural to her: to her old husband it was no more natural than if the . . . .

What happened next happened so quickly that she had no time to escape. The first blow fell across her shoulders, forcing her to her knees and thus giving the old man another chance to strike again. He rained blow after blow on her with his crook, venting his whole anger, his wrath on her, cursing her with all the words he could muster. "You . . . you, haven't you any shame at all? You . . . you just stand there like . . . like a stone and watch me struggling here like . . . ." The crook broke in two. Now the old man seemed as if he would devour her; he was biting his fingers in bitter anger. But the whole thing was over now. Now he had to swallow the left-overs of his anger. Nevertheless, he had now disposed of some of the wrath and anger which had lain heavily on him for such a long time. Gaciku lay there beside him, whimpering and whining miserably, involuntarily offering him her body to drum as much as he wanted: only now he was too weak.

"Ahaa", he hissed his relief now that he had exercised his husbandhood. Things do take the wrong course sometimes. It is natural. When this happens, somebody is needed to put these things on the right course again. For example, things were taking the wrong course as far as Gaciku was concerned. She was underestimating her husband. She was forgetting him, and what he was capable of doing—and this neglect of hers was disturbing and disrupting. Things had needed someone at that time to right them, to direct them into the usual and accepted channel. He had been there, thanks to the coincidence of fate or whatever it was. What he had done to her was what needed to be done, the obvious, the only thing that could have been done. He had done his best, thus putting matters right again. She wouldn't underestimate him again as long as she lived.

"Shooooo", he hissed again, knocking his snuff bottle with his baccy-stained thumb. He took a pinch and inhaled hard through his wide nostrils. "Ahaaa." This seemed to send his head working along the right lines. "Now to that other problem", he thought seriously: the dilemma for which he had decided to wake up; the dilemma which was putting some madness into his head. "Hey, wake up! Don't just lie there like a bride. Go and bring me my 'things'. I've got to go. Quickly, woman", he commanded. "Things?" She had not heard properly. He—this crazy old bull—surely didn't mean the "things" with which he performed his sacrifices and rituals? But that was exactly what he did mean. "So after

171

all he is still determined to see this business through.
So he still won't give up." This made her forget the beating
she had absorbed earlier and she quickly disappeared.

Funny how they all obeyed him. He was now old,
much too old to be of any use to them, his wives. The
younger ones, indeed, were now freely bearing children
by outsiders. He was too old now to have the honour of
being called a "man". Yet, despite all this, his wives
obeyed him and paid attention to his every wish, just as
much as before. There was that in his whole being—a
kind of radiant menace in his eyes—which sent their
knees buckling the minute he reared up. And, in addition
to this, there was some kind of strength—not the kind
of strength boxers and wrestlers are equipped with,
but the kind of strength an antelope's hind hooves carry:
intangible, strong, solid, pure strength, hidden in bones
and very unlike the naked, physical strength in muscles—
a strength which made his wives know him for what he
was. They obeyed him, his wives, without objection,
without complaints, like little children their teacher.
And when things took the wrong direction, he righted
them for them—for both his and their well-being.

Gaciku brought him his tools in a hide bag. She
seemed to have completely forgotten the previous episode.
She was used to this kind of life, poor woman. Slowly,
weakly, he managed to put himself on his feet, with her
beside him. He slung the hide bag across his shoulder
and supported himself with a stick. Gaciku witnessed
all this struggle of his and it did touch her heart. She
gave him a very sympathetic look which demonstrated
her love for him. "Are you really going? I mean . . .
aren't you feeling very sick?", she said, unsure of herself.
"No. It is most important that I go. I must go." Hesitatingly, he picked his steps and walked out of the mud hut.
She watched him go with a mixture of feelings: she was
happy he had left the hut, thus bringing to an end the
constant, unjustified, unpredictable scoldings and beatings
for a while; but she was sad to see him go there so weak,

and he wouldn't hear of the idea of giving up the journey. She was entitled to such feelings. She was a woman and it is a part of woman's make-up to feel that way.

As she watched him disappear into the cloak of the distance, she wondered if the god would listen to his prayers—and, if he did listen at all, would he accept them and save them from the abuse and threats of their neighbours? Would he? As she watched him drag his feet away, she was almost sure something strange would follow. Immediately she turned back and went to tell the other wives about it.

Slowly, carefully, almost like a little child, he planted one foot after the other onto the grinded, soft dust. Every time Mwangi put his foot down, a cloud of dust would whirl upwards, provoked, and then would settle down peacefully as he passed. This dust was warm and soft like ashes, dry as powder. His old, soft feet felt its constant stings but he didn't seem to mind this at all. His spine was bowed permanently by years; age had now deprived him of the best part of his once-strong muscles, leaving him as his sole right the mastership of a soft, wrinkled skin which faithfully coated his weak old bones. His hide bag rested on his back, his right hand clung to his crook while his left hand held limply to his back. The sun was hot—too hot for Mwangi—but its heat did not succeed in extracting one drop of sweat from his inside. There was no sweat in him: age had dried it all. The whole picture of him was awestriking, reverent and, somehow, there seemed to be something holy about him. You felt that if Mwangi had met a lion, perhaps it wouldn't have so much as scratched his old skin: partly because of his thinness, and partly because of the holiness about him. With defiant boldness, this age-soaked figure walked on, indefatigably.

For many years he had been the village rainmaker. He had inherited this skill from his father and now, according to the custom, he was supposed to leave the skill to his eldest son. Mwangi was determined to see that the skill, as his father had told him, remained within the household. It was his wish that after his "going-away" his son Ngugi should take over. Ngugi would continue from then on, and when his day to "go away" came, he would pass the skill on to his son. And if he, Ngugi, had no son, then the skill would cross the boundary and would be left in the hands of Njau—Mwangi's second son. It would go on like that for years on end, for fate alone knew how long it had already been going on and how long this talent had been within the household; how old it was and from which great-grandfather it really had descended.

But fate, which always plays a great part in our lives, had its own way. A Father John whose characteristics and way of life were ominously different from theirs; whose beliefs and ideas were, as Mwangi expressed it, "heinous"; who, they said, had come from afar with charms whose power had no equal in the village, had come in the wake of Mwangi's thoughts. It was this strange man, Father John, who had bewitched his eldest son, Ngugi, away from Mwangi.

When the rains were long overdue, people would come to Mwangi, the rainmaker, and would ask him if anything was the matter with the rain-god. "Yes", Mwangi would tell them gravely. Such and such a person didn't contribute anything towards the god's sacrifice last season. Or such-and-such stole a bag of peas from so-and-so—the bag which was meant for the god last winter. That was a heinous crime as far as the rain-god was concerned. "Oh, what shall we do, Mwangi? The god will castigate us!" "Yes", Mwangi would answer with feeling. "He will unless he is appeased and this should be done soon." And here Mwangi would name all sorts of things he really wanted and the people, having nothing more to do, would willingly, yet a little doubtfully, succumb to Mwangi's wishes at once. And so Mwangi would pick his path reverently to the sacred place, the home of the rain-god. And what went on there nobody ever knew, for Mwangi was always alone there with his bag of tools.

It is incredible and hard to believe—perhaps luck wanted it this way, or perhaps it was coincidence—but the fact remains that whenever Mwangi went there it would be rain that would send him running home. There had never been a day when Mwangi had gone there and had come walking home undrenched with rain. And when he came back to the waiting villagers, they would lift him off his feet, hug him and sing him hero's songs, and then would give him gifts, just out of happiness. And the rain would go on rhythmically for days on end. And Mwangi would be happy and contented. He would sit on his three-legged stool with his bag of tools near him, stroking his snuff-bottle contentedly and would watch the drops of rain as, relentlessly and in succession, they fell from God's Palace. There he would sit musing, happy with himself, just like a surgeon after a successful operation. This was life, he would muse. It was supposed to be this way. Things were taking the right course now. It was supposed to stream down properly, like this.

But, with the coming of Father John, things had abruptly gone adrift, astray. It had all started when this Father John (God alone knew what kind of children he had fathered—this lonely, solitary man without a wife), started hammering into the villagers' heads this crazy story of a true God, a God who, as he said, was the most God, the holiest, purest God Father John had ever known. He said that his God was the life-maker, life-disposer and, in fact, He was the maker of all things—even the rain. At the mention of "rain" a sudden nightmare had got hold of Mwangi and gradually it has developed into an indescribable illness. His god had been abused. And from then on, he never left his hide bed; he was always lying there with fever—a kind of fever all the village "doctors" were unable to cure. In the end everybody kept quiet and hoped for the best. And Father John went on preaching the Gospel to them. And then the rainy season came and found Mwangi on his bed, unable to so much as lift his finger.

Now the villagers were wondering. They were torn between two gods, between two faiths. Now everybody was waiting eagerly, curiously, to see—to see what they had never seen before. "Wonders will never cease", they said to each other. Here was Mwangi the rainmaker lying on his hide bed more dead than alive; here were the fields still parched with drought; and here finally was Father John preaching that the true God would send the rains as usual to His people—He above, the Holy one. Well now, would Mwangi wake up from his illness and go to the sacred place? Would Father John's God send rain? Yes, a different rain perhaps. Mwangi had declined to make any comments on the subject. This was attributed to his indisposition. But would it ever rain?

Slowly the days slid smoothly away. And with each passing day, the villagers' curiosity gathered momentum. And then one day, quite unpredictably, without the slightest warning at all, it rained. And people, instead of talking and taking sides, kept mum, perhaps with wonderment, perhaps with awe, perhaps with excitement or, most probably, with confusion.

On that occasion Mwangi had remained on his bed; his fever had gathered strength. He looked like an old, shapeless, bag of bones—solid, hard bones but without gristle. And then, as if this was not enough of a blow, his eldest son, Ngugi, went over to Father John's side. Things *were* taking the wrong course now. Things were really going adrift. Mwangi nearly died that year, but his day was not due yet.

———————

Now he was walking rhythmically, not hurrying and not hesitating. He looked as if he would collapse any moment under his bag of tools. His head was filled with thoughts. Just recently, he had heard people despising him; people talking bad of him; people saying that the rain-god was no longer listening to his prayers, that he was no longer accepting his sacrifices. "What has he done to the god?" they asked each other. Mwangi had listened with a heavy heart. This was a terrible threat to his life and would be ruin to his family. All this was caused by that Father John. He was responsible for everything. Mwangi was determined to see the end of him. It was evident that some of the villagers were now siding with Father John. His charms appeared to be strong enough to have been able to change the villagers' thoughts and faith. When his son Ngugi denounced the rain-god and took to Father John, Mwangi had nearly died from shock. But luckily he had been able to control his astonishment although his fever had increased a little. He knew people would flock into his hut after this, and ask him questions; so, even when he felt much better, he feigned fever so as to be left alone with his thoughts. At present he felt confused, but he knew what he had to do in future. If Father John succeeded—which now seemed probable—then the villagers would either drive Mwangi away or would kill him. He had been exploiting them a great deal, they would say, demanding endless sacrifices. Nevertheless Mwangi felt that he had faith enough in his rain-god. His god wouldn't let him down; it had never let him down before and he was sure it wouldn't now. As for that season when it had rained without his having gone to pray to the god and make sacrifices, well that had happened accidentally, he comforted himself. Even food sometimes goes down the wrong throat.

This was the moment he had been waiting for—the rainy season. As he ambled along the dusty path, he knew the fight was on and that he had to show Father John what he was capable of doing—and the villagers too. How on earth could they lend their ears to a stranger —a man whose skin was very different from their own; a man whose language they didn't understand; a man they knew not where and when he came from or where he was heading? How could they succumb to his temptations so quickly as that, like children? How could they? This he attributed to the wrong course things had taken. He would right them. He would. And teach the villagers a lesson they wouldn't forget. Even when things went wrong in his home, he taught the culprit a lesson: Gaciku. This was the only way to put things running on the right course again. As he lay weakly on his hide bed, he made up his mind to wake up and go to the sacred place.

"I will go, go there and pray", Mwangi thought as he hiked on in the scorching sun. "I'll invoke the god to stop the rains for a month. I must delay them. It will teach the villagers a good lesson. It'll put things right again. Like Gaciku, they won't underestimate me again. I must stop the rain. I will stop the rain." And with that strong faith, and obsessed by these thoughts, he walked on, oblivious of the environment, the sun and the burning dust.

Gaciku and the other wives gathered together and instead of talking, exchanging ideas, they kept quiet, each in her own thoughts. They waited—waited eagerly for anything to happen. They were torn between fear and happiness. Fear, because the whole village now knew that their husband had gone to pray for the rains to come and, if the rains didn't come, if his god failed him, the results would be fearful. This made their backs shudder uncontrollably. And happiness, because Mwangi had plucked up courage to go after all. If he had not gone, if it had rained without his prayers like last season, then what would happen to the whole family was even more frightening.

Gloriously, like a woman returning home after a hard day's work, the sun walked homewards and gradually disappeared behind the horizon. Suddenly it became dark, much too dark. And then, without warning, they saw the flashing sign and heard the deafening thunder. Then they saw it. It was as if it was feeling shame . . . a drop . . . then a minute's interval . . . and then another drop. Then it came, the whole of it without a break.

It came with its children. Rain. Cold, comforting and tender rain.

Now the whole world was filled with shouts, singing and dances. Everybody was making merry, happy as happy can be, and glad that the long-awaited rain had come—it was very symbolic of the birth of a baby boy. They sang and danced for hours on end, into the night, without stopping, drunk with happiness. They waited expectantly to welcome Mwangi home, to lift him off his feet and to give him gifts. He had succeeded after all—they thought. Father John, to them, didn't exist. His god or gods might go to hell as far as they were concerned. They knew Mwangi, understood him and his language, and accepted him because he was one of them. Soon he would come home to them, their Mwangi they would hug him and accord him a hero's welcome. They would. And then things would go on as usual, and they wouldn't listen to Father John at all. They would even chase him away from their village. They waited happily, expectantly, for Mwangi. Only Mwangi never came home to them again. The rains had indeed broken.

The hooting owl

As soon as I woke up that morning, I detected something strange in the morning air. It was something peculiar, something unearthly, something dreadful. I saw it, I smelt it, and I felt it in my body. Yet I couldn't really see it. I was at a loss to describe it and to make out exactly what it really was. But it was there, nevertheless, bright as day and in black and white.

Perhaps it was because the previous night when, in a dream, I had urinated on the bed clothes, my mother had threatened to send me out to be sliced and swallowed up by that ghost-like, strong giant who always enjoyed young children like me for his supper. Or perhaps it was because another boy, the previous day, had jokingly tried to dip me in that awful, revered hole in the stem of that sacred tree. Whatever the cause, it was working on me now, creating a strange feeling, a vision inside me, making me re-live and re-experience those dreadful, gone moments.

My mother called me out for breakfast: I had no appetite; I felt like running away from everybody. In the end, when she had failed to make me eat the food, she put it in the little basket she had made for me, and made me carry it with me to the fields—those savannahs—grassy, vast, endless fields where we used to drive our cattle for grazing.

I hurriedly joined the other boys and, equipping myself with a little club, a crook and that little bag of food slung across my shoulder, with my little motor-tyre-made sandals properly fitted on my feet, we slowly walked behind the herd of cattle, whistling and singing some lyrics to the animals—a herdsman's language to his animals and a language my old grandfather had taken considerable time and effort to teach me.

Just before we were out of the compound, and merely out of curiosity, my instinct told me to look back. Consequently I threw my eyes back. I was in time to see my father come out of my grandfather's hut and pace the ground slowly, showing every sign of unhappiness, lost completely in thoughts as if only his powerful body were in this world and his mind and soul were in another world. Then my mother, as if from nowhere, joined him and, very strangely, held his massive paws in hers—something I had never seen her do before—as if she were beseeching him to protect her from an invisible antagonist. He stopped pacing the ground and I could see that they were both very strongly affected by an emotional, sentimental talk. Then my mother looked down, as if with shame, and then hid her face and, to my horror, without being told, it clicked in me, young as I was, that she was actually crying.

Even when my father beat her, I never saw her cry. Perhaps it was because it always happened in the hut and when she finally came out a young child like me was never any the wiser.

"That's a dreadful cut you have on your face, mother", I used to remark sympathetically, whenever I found her face swelling, or her leg limping, after my father had beaten her. "Yes, my child", she would answer with feeling. "It was Ngunu, that horrible, untameable cow when I tried to milk it last night. Its horns are as quick and sharp as your father's spear; its kick is no lighter than your father's blow: your father is strong you know."

"Yes, mother, I know." And with that well-presented bluff, my curiosity would be quenched and I would keep quiet, staring at her with every kind of sympathy, cursing that "untameable cow" which had hurt her, and wishing badly that I were strong enough to handle that animal myself.

As the dewy, serpentine, forked paths—herdsmen's paths—distanced me from my home, I felt that strange impact inside me gather momentum. More so because just a few minutes ago I had seen my mother cry. I felt lonely, an outcast; I experienced the loneliness of an orphan, in spite of the fact that I was amidst boys, and bigger boys at that. I felt my body grow weak with time and my knees felt like knocking against each other under me. This momentary nightmare got so strong a hold on me that I felt like bawling my head off with inexplicable, torturing fright. Why was I like this? So miserable, so weak? What was wrong—was it me or the world or whatever was it? I couldn't help thinking hard and trying to figure things out. And presently I saw things; things had been happening without my taking them into account, without my regarding them seriously. Firstly, for example; whenever the darkness descended, after giving us our food, my mother and father would casually, yet surreptitiously, go out of the hut and, joining my other relatives, would steal into my grandfather's hut. None of them had any idea that I knew where they went but, nevertheless, I knew perfectly well. However, the fact that they went so quietly, with every imaginable sign of solemnity, whetted my curiosity so much that I felt it my right to know exactly what the matter was.

And, secondly, my grandfather had been away—out of sight—for a long time. His hut was always locked and none of us little ones was allowed to play near it— which had been our wont.

My grandmother had died long ago. My grandfather had demeaned himself—sort of volunteered himself devotedly—and had taken her place: that is, he never tired of telling us short stories in the evening. He even had the nerve to sing us some lyrics, some verses which go hand in hand with short stories. His voice was rough, hoarse in comparison with grandmother's but, nevertheless, he had love enough to sing for us—which was not a man's job. I used to stare fascinated at that bony old skull of his and could never find an answer to the question as to where those riddles after riddles, legends and epics really came from—from which corner of his big, wrinkled pate that wisdom came and how deep and wide was that reservoir?

Whenever we were in the fields, we longed hungrily for the evening to descend so that we could drive the cattle home and, after that, sit by the fire and listen to our grandfather lull us to sleep with sweet stories. The other children from the neighbourhood sometimes joined us around the fire and very willingly, just like ourselves, lent my grandfather their little ears to be crammed with the lyrical sounds of the old man's voice. At this moment I was all happiness because I could boss them and bully those children from the neighbourhood without any one of them raising so much as a finger to oppose me. None of them, not even the bigger ones, could dare utter an abusive word to me in opposition to my selfish actions. The fact that I was at my home and they were the intruders always protected me invincibly on such occasions. And it was from this situation that I derived that comforting, empowering feeling which always makes a boy feel competent and masculine and have that reassuring warmth of being a he-man one day.

And now, all of a sudden, without the slightest warning at all, my grandfather disappears into thin air and I don't see him again nor am I allowed to play near his compound—the whole, beautiful world of mine suddenly changes and crashes into emptiness because of my grandfather's absence.

As I ambled slowly along behind the cattle, my body fell automatically into its daily rhythm of walking to which it had become used after much practice. But my mind, rather than regarding and trying to determine the environment, fell into thinking and trying to analyse the invisible, mysterious apparition at home. My missing grandfather was now paining me like the irritation on one's skin after a vermin has helped itself to one's blood. Whatever this thing at home was, whether it had any connection with the mysterious disappearance of my grandfather or not, I felt sure that it was gathering strength; it was reaching its peak. For wasn't my mother always gloomy nowadays? Wasn't my father always quite reserved and quiet? Had I not seen my mother hold my father's hand in hers like a child—and had I not seen her cry after that? Certainly I had. I longed terribly to be a grown-up, for then I would have been told everything about everything. What was wrong? Had it anything to do with my grandfather? Was he . . . was he sick? I could only know this by asking my mother.

That day in the fields was long, dreadful and seemed endless and when it finally came to an end, I ran rather than walked homewards. When at last I got home to mother, the vermin, which had been biting me all the time, bit me a little too much and I could hold myself back no longer. I knew I had been warned against asking questions many a time; I knew that she would be annoyed: but I was not the obedient, biddable boy I used to be; the nightmare had changed me.

Little did I then realise that this particular curiosity of mine, this asking of strange questions on such an occasion would later become a confirmed legend—a legend which found no better place to stay than on the lips of women, passing from one pair of lips to another, gathering momentum, strength and interest, so that whenever a woman told it to her companion, she distorted it in such a way that it always acquired new words, new phrases and a new meaning altogether—making me the centre of admiration, envy and reverence; a highly promising hero. "The boy is a born hero." "You only say 'a hero'?" "Don't you have the eyes to see that he is a born hero and a leader as well?" "Oh, who was it who said that there are people who have got eyes and don't see, and ears with which they don't hear? Who was it? How right he was! You women—you beautiful belles—interest me. You talk merely of heroism and leadership as if you didn't hear the *prophetic* accent, quality, with which the boy asked those questions which were in fact beyond his age. Can't you see the vivid characteristics of a prophet—can't you see a real born prophet in him?"

"Mother, you have to tell me! Where did our grand-father go?" So I had come out with it at last. I felt as if a heavy load had been lifted off my shoulders for a while. I sighed and rested, as if under a tree to cool myself, and waited expectantly for my answer which, for all I knew, might possibly be in the form either of more words or of a spank.

"Stop it, child!", Mother bawled. "How many times do I . . . All right, I see you have inherited your father's obstinacy. I see. A lamb takes after its mother, so they say, and how right they are! All right, child, listen. Your grandfather went to see a famous witch-doctor who stays in the village yonder. Now if you ask questions again, that witch-doctor will be annoyed with you and will turn you into anything he fancies—you may be turned into a girl for all he cares. And if you are turned into a girl, of course the other girls won't accept you as one of them. And the boys will surely . . . ." "No! No! I don't want that! No! I'll keep quiet, mother! I will! I promise!" "That's good."

Miserable as I was, yet when she uttered those three words I couldn't help detecting some very strange change in her voice. Her voice had dramatically acquired a new tone; it had a kind of loneliness which was extreme-ly touching, appealing—it was the voice from a heart labouring under a great strain. I looked into her eyes and in spite of myself I sympathised with her—and that brought me back to where I was minutes ago. What had happened? What was wrong? Why had her voice changed so? I wanted badly to ask, but the fear of being turned into a girl made itself strong within me. "That's good, my child", she said, let go a deep sigh of relaxation, and then kept quiet. And that was all I could get from her. This only helped to sharpen my curiosity.

After I had promised my mother that I wouldn't ask any more questions, she seemed content and set about doing her household chores; but inside I was flaming with curiosity. Her refusal to answer my questions had only succeeded in whetting this curiosity. And so I vowed—or, rather, was forced by this power to vow—to the world that, risky as it was, I had to get an answer to the mystery. I had to know where my parents went every night and what they were doing with that awe-inspiring air of solemnity about them. To declare my seriousness I had to take an oath, as was our normal custom on such occasions. So slowly I picked my steps to where the ash was heaped. I moistened my pointing finger with saliva and touched some ash with it, and then I put it on my tongue. Then I faced the setting sun and, standing thus, I crossed my forehead with the ashy finger with which finally I made a sign across my throat symbolic of a knife cutting it. This was accompanied by some incantations. "May a knife come from heaven and cut my throat and may I perish with the setting sun if I don't fulfil the obligation for which I have taken this solemn oath." After this ritual was over, the sun slowly disappeared and a gust of wind sent me back home.

At home I waited patiently for the time to come. I knew exactly what I had to do. Finally the long-awaited moment came. After giving us food, my mother put a headscarf on her head and after making sure that everything was as it should be, she casually followed my father, who had already preceded her outside. No sooner were they outside than I started tailing them. Hiding myself in a corner, I watched as my parents, together with my relatives, entered, slowly, one by one, my grandfather's hut. When they were all gone, I sneaked stealthily and stood near my grandfather's crooked door. The door was so old, so worn out, that I was perfectly able to see inside, through the cracks. The hut was occupied by more than ten people, yet it was more like a grave with its dead, frightening silence. It was as if the occupants were standing before the sacred tree, reverent, trying to placate an angry god. So solemn were they that a shiver of fear ran down my spine and made me shudder all over. I tried vainly to flatten my body against the mud wall to command some courage, but my legs failed me; slowly I slid uncontrollably down to the floor with fear, and shrank into a heap. I sat down near the door and watched through a crack. I saw them bring near the fire a kind of bed from the dark corner of the hut. A heap of ruffled clothes was on top of it. All this time I had not seen my grandfather—the main object of my coming here. I was beginning to agree with mother that my grandfather had really gone to see a witch-doctor. I was losing hope of ever seeing him again. But just then it happened.

They started undoing the heap of clothes on the bed which was on the floor. One by one they removed them, slowly, reverently, with every air of solemnity. Then I saw it. The apparition which I saw will never be out of my mind; on the bed lay the body of a man, so skeletony, so flabby, so withered that it looked like the body of a child. Just then, somewhere in the darkness, an owl went into a sudden fit of hooting and then the hooting subsided as quickly as it had come. Was it coincidence that an owl should wail at this particular moment? No, it was no coincidence at all. For had my grandmother not told us that when an owl cries something ominous might follow? Fear started getting a stronger hold on me. The whole thing started giving me the creeps. Apart from the ossified body on the floor, nobody else seemed to hear the hooting—or were they just trying to bluff the dying man perhaps? The withered body, however, seemed to gather courage with the hooting of the owl; it gesticulated frantically, weakly, throwing its bony hands into the air and twisting its thin lips into gibberish, inaudible speech. They crowded near it, awe-stricken, and tried to make out the scattered, inaudible words the man was uttering. And then the owl hooted again; this time it was duly heard. The men flocked out of the hut in a hurry and each went his own way. Whether they saw me crouched at the corner and took me for a dog, nobody knows, but the point is that somebody nearly walked over me. The atmosphere which had been peaceful and quiet a minute ago was now filled with shouts and the noise of men trying in vain to locate the crying owl in order to chase it away. The owl never stopped hooting. It went on moaning as if its child was dead. My grandmother had told me before she had died that at this time the owl must be beaten and chased away with eggs only; and not with stones. Why was this? I never learned the answer.

The fear of the occasion, the fear of what might result after its hooting, gripped me so hard that, having no alternative, I let go a shrieking bawl and then beat it to our hut. On reaching it, I found that the hut was as dark and empty as outside. Fear overcame me. I felt totally confused. It was only natural, therefore, that I should resort to my mother's protection and affection. So I fled speedily to my grandfather's hut where I knew my mother to be. As I was about to enter I found myself head to head with my mother. Her body stopped me and held it so firmly that I forced her into immobility; she stood still, flabbergasted and perhaps fearful, while I shook like a leaf, breathing like a mad rhino.

"Why, where have you been?" Even as she talked, in spite of myself, I discovered that she was undergoing great fear. I was gasping for breath and before I could answer, she said, "Come, I have been looking for you." I let go my hold on her body. I felt like running away. Why? What was wrong with . . . with the world . . . with everybody? Or was it the gods? Why was everything, everybody incomprehensible, changing so strangely? And now I cursed my curiosity. Perhaps if I had not tried to interfere, things would still have been as they were before. Perhaps the owl wouldn't have hooted. Perhaps my grandfather wouldn't have come back from the witch-doctor's home so sick. Perhaps he wouldn't have asked for me. Perhaps . . . perhaps. Why had I tried to spy? Perhaps the witch-doctor had seen me and was going to turn me into a girl. Was that why I was being called? "Mother . . . ." I wanted to tell her everything, to confess to her and get it over with. "Mother . . . I . . . I." She was already dragging me inside. Whether I liked it or not, I had to command some courage and act like a brave man now. It was my turn.

On entering the hut, all the women held their breath, sighed solemnly and kept mum. My mother led me to where the old man lay, more dead than alive. I was told to kneel down. I did.

"Grandfather, this is me, Barasa", I said with a weak, fading voice, fighting back tears. Slowly, with effort, the old man stretched his hand towards me; I held it in mine and the very thinness of it made me nearly run out of my skin.

"Bar . . . Bar . . . ra . . . Barasa", he started with an unnaturally polite, weak voice. Apart from the bawling and shouting outside, the world was dead quiet. The women controlled their breath and knelt down reverently, with feeling. And the old man talked.

"I knew I would see you be . . . before I was gone . . . before it was all over. But . . . but . . . they wouldn't let me see you . . . they wouldn't. Anyway, that is neither here nor there." The voice was with effort controlled, quick, appealing, and had that taste of finality.

If I had been old and wise, I could have detected the message—the goodbye message—the voice carried; I could have known that the voice came from the depth of his heart and that sooner or later the heart would go weak and be empty of the power which helped to manufacture the words and the voice. But I didn't know. To me it was a day-to-day, grandfather to grandson talk.

I had never seen a dead or dying man before. I didn't know what it was to die; I didn't know when one was dead or when one was unconscious. All I knew was that when one dies one "goes home to rest forever". I fought back tears and held the old man's hand firmly. He continued.

"May . . . may . . . may the Creator look after you well after I am gone. For you are the sole guard of this home. My . . . my beloved boy, look after your brothers and sisters. Look after . . . after your home properly. Look after the cattle, look after your mothers, look after . . . after . . . oh . . . ehee."

The weak, thin hand in mine slowly grew weaker and weaker and then started to grow cold. I held it much firmer, fighting against emotions and tears. The women faced the wall and, hiding their faces in their hands, each one of them was carried away by scalding tears. I gazed at them idiotically, confusedly, and then looked down at the sick man and waited expectantly for him to talk more. But the lips, which a minute ago had been occupied by live words, were now parted, never to meet again. The teeth were firmly clenched. Somewhere, far away outside, a moaning owl was hooting its head off. Somewhere outside, my father was cursing his head off, trying to chase away the wailing, ominous owl, oblivious of what was going on in his father's hut. And here, in my own world, I held tenderly, affectionately, the hand of the one man I had loved, the man I had been missing, scarcely knowing that the man who had once been my grandfather was no more than a corpse—no more alive than a quarry stone.

Incredibly, as if by way of warning, the owl stopped hooting abruptly. Naturally the shouts and curses outside came to a full stop. And the world went dead with silence. Slowly, with controlled disgust, I went to my mother and whispered, "He has refused to talk to me again mother. He is angry." "Yes, son, I know", she said, controlling tears. "He has gone with the hooting owl;

he will come back some day—in another form."

My fight against my emotions, against my tears was over now. I cried and sobbed with disgust and confusion.

That night saw the legend, "When the owl hoots at night, it is the harbinger of death", come true.

Later, when I was of age, I learned why I had not been allowed to see my grandfather. My parents' sincere love for me was so strong that although my grandfather had demanded to see me for a long time, they wouldn't let me see him; they wouldn't even let me play near his hut, lest he should hear my voice and call me.

This did not mean that they didn't love my grandfather at all. But, after seeing the symptoms of his diseases, it had soon become apparent that the old man was not going to live long—"his days were numbered". And so my parents were very afraid that, if I saw the thinness, the flabbiness of his body, if I saw the haunting weak eyes, the wrinkled, ghost-like face, I might have had nightmares in my sleep—nightmares with which I might have to live throughout my life; nightmares which might spoil my days of youth.

Pride and prejudice

Njoroge emerged from his hut rather hurriedly and ran, rather than walked, a little distance to a bush. Then suddenly he stopped, sat abruptly on his heels and supported himself with his stick. Around his waist ran a leather belt on which hung the sheath of his sword. He knew it was there, sharp as a razor; nevertheless, he put his hand around its hilt and felt it. "Ah", he sighed contentedly, and continued with the work which had brought him there—urinating. And when he was finished, a thought struck him. "Yes", he thought to himself, "my son is another lion. When he roars, every man trembles a little. Fine. But the boy worries me as he seems to know nothing about 'she-goats'. How . . . how . . . can he be so . . . Ah . . . anyway. But I must do something about it. This . . . this new age!"

He was in such deep thought that he forgot the posture in which he was sitting until he was interrupted by a sharp whistle. This brought him suddenly into reality again. Abruptly he turned round to see if anybody had seen him and, as he turned round, his knees cracked. "Eh", he muttered to himself, "old age really is a disease."

Njenga was pacing the ground outside Njoroge's hut. Njoroge hoped that Njenga had not seen him urinating, so he feigned surprise. "Eh", he began, "I wasn't expecting you! Did your wife chase you away? I haven't even washed my eyebrows. I had gone for a while to survey my land. How is your compound?" Njenga purposely ignored all that and said, "You do your surveying sitting down, do you? You must have done quite a lot of surveying. I arrived here when you were sitting there like an old baboon and I've been waiting for you to finish the . . . er . . . surveying." And with that, Njenga threw back his head and laughed loudly. Njoroge drew his eyebrows together, stared at his friend, then slowly shook his head in a gesture of negation. He was annoyed, but Njenga was his age-mate and convention had given him the right to say whatever he wanted.

"Let's go inside", Njoroge invited Njenga.

Once inside, Njoroge gave his visitor a stool to sit on. Then he called out to his wives for something to eat. But Njenga protested. "I left my wives at home. If I had needed food, they would have given it to me. The only thing they can't give me is snuff. That's why I came out here so early. If you would be so kind as to give me some snuff, I won't stay here more than a minute."

Njoroge looked at his friend in silent appraisal. Had it been another man, Njoroge wouldn't have been so quiet, so tolerant. He wouldn't have accepted that kind of speech from another man. But Njenga was different: he was immune.

Njoroge handed his snuff bottle over to his friend. Njenga took the bottle, poured some snuff onto his palm and then gave the bottle back to Njoroge who, likewise, poured some onto his hand and then put the bottle between his two fingers. He inhaled a pinch of snuff hard through his nostrils. "Ah", he sighed. "Look", he said over the snuff, "you are old, I am old, why can't we be our age, and talk seriously for a while."

"Go on, old man", Njenga invited.

"The case of my son has puzzled me. Tell me what to do", Njoroge said.

———

Happy and memorable and gone were the good old days when Njoroge, as a hero and as a good, sociable man with an impeccable reputation, was very well known by his clan. Because of his bravery, he had fought and won countless battles during his youth. This had conveyed far his fame, as far as to the other, neighbouring tribes.

Those were the good old days when women sang his praises whenever they gathered, and men found it a great honour to share a drink with him. And, as if on purpose, God had extended these happy days by giving Njoroge a baby boy as his first-born. The praises were sung all the more; the goats, sheep and bulls were slaughtered continuously to make these good days yet more memorable. Countless gourds of sugar-cane wine were emptied into men's dry throats to make life yet more lively and stimulating.

And with the wine-drinking and praise-singing, with the fighting and bearing of children, the good days regrettably slipped away, never to come back. And with the running away of the good days, people became laden with years—the old grew older and the unborn were finally born. And Njoroge soon found himself with mature boys and girls ready to be betrothed.

Then Njoroge relived the good, gone days again, when his son turned out to be a great hero. Nganga led warriors and fought battles which he never lost. People talked much. Women worshipped him and the girls, falling head over heels in love with him, yearned terribly for him—but never got him. The young men envied him while the old prayed to him to strike the enemy still harder. And Njoroge, right in the background, watched his son cause havoc in the land of his enemy and earn himself praises, and he was contented, reassured and happy. "I did the same", he muttered to himself. "The boy is following in my footsteps. It is well." And it was well. He saw himself in his son and was happy.

That was—or so it seemed to Njoroge—a long time ago. Those days and their happiness had suddenly vanished, never to be seen again. That leaf of life had withered and wilted away and a new one, of a different sort, had now taken its place.

All of Njoroge's sons had found themselves wives; all of his daughters had found themselves husbands. But Nganga, his beloved, his pride, remained as single as ever—and so did his sister Wambui. Wambui, a faithful honest sister to her brother and her family, had good and acceptable reasons: she would get married to her suitor as soon as her brother had found himself a spouse so that her—Wambui's—bride-price could be handed over to her brother's in-laws, thus bestowing a great and recognised honour on both her brother and her family. That was understandable. But Nganga's was an insoluble problem—a problem which was making his father's head spin like a top.

"It's this son of mine, Nganga", Njoroge told his friend matter-of-factly. He sniffed hard another pinch of *mbaki* from his palm. "When a girl gets out of hand", he continued, "it is always natural that people blame her mother. Although the father is sometimes included, he is not so much involved as the mother—because that is considered to be a mother's affair. But a son, a grown-up son, is a different case. It's the father who carries the blame. Sooner or later, people will start blaming my son on me. Here is a son—a big, grown-up son—who has already proved his worth. A son who comes of a noble family—a good-looking, healthy son. Here is a proud father who would be offered shelter and a drink in every homestead he happened to pass. A prominent father whom any man would like to call 'in-law'." Here he paused to give life to the discourse. Then he continued in regretful tones. "How come then that the son—the first-born of the home—has reached such an age without a wife? People will ask each other: 'What kind of a father is that—a father who can't get his son a wife?' And then they will start gossiping all over the place. Some will defend me and say that the boy is old and good-looking enough to find himself a thousand wives. And that will start them wondering why the son hasn't married one single wife so far, let alone a thousand. Why? And God knows, they won't hesitate to call my son a eunuch—the impotent hero of their time who couldn't get himself a wife." Njoroge spat out his anger and stared at the spittle unseeingly.

"Have you talked to him about this?", Njenga asked concernedly.

"A thousand times", Njoroge answered bitterly. "It's no use talking to him now. I have even sent him a *kiama*, but all he says to this delegation is that he will get married when the right time comes. All he's interested in is battle. To fight and to kill. You can't imagine how worried I am, and how perturbed. Supposing he happens to fight a losing battle? Supposing he gets killed in a battle? Nobody to carry on the threads of his fame. I am growing old now, and the more I think of it all the older and more broken-hearted do I feel. I feel my happy days in the world are now over. Good were the old, gone days when I was known for what I was." Here he lapsed into silence. For a long time they sat there quiet: even the *mbakī* was now forgotten. The train of their thoughts had taken them back to those old, gone days of their youth. "They are gone", Njoroge said, more to himself than to Njenga. "Those good days are gone for ever. If anything happens to my son now . . . ."

"Have you visited the *mūndū mūgo*?" Njenga asked with feeling.

"No", Njoroge answered.

"You had better go. He's sometimes helpful."

"No", Njoroge admitted, "I had not thought of him."

With a long sniffing of his snuff, Njenga took leave of his friend, promising to come back later and dwell on the subject more seriously.

"Mother, I am worried about my brother", Wambui said to her mother in girlish tones. "He never seems to think of getting married."

"Don't judge him too harshly, my daughter", the mother said to her daughter. "He must get married some time. Are you still doing what I told you to do?"

"Yes, mother", Wambui answered. "Yesterday I came home with three girls from the village yonder. I made them meet him and I introduced them to him although they already knew him. I'm always bringing girls home every time I get the chance."

"And you haven't seen any signs of any changes in your brother yet?"

"No, my brother only greets them, and then walks out, saying that he has important business to see to. No girl so far has seemed to take his fancy, and I will not get married to Kariuki until my brother gets a wife. I can't leave him like this." The mother and the daughter mused quietly for a while. Then as an after-thought, the mother said, "No girl has so much as excited him? You mean not one single girl at all?"

"Not that I know of, mother . . . er . . . no . . . no."

"No what? You are stammering. You are not sure of yourself."

"No, but . . . but that girl you told me not to be with."

"What girl? Wairimu? Yes, indeed. It is your father who hates her because of her father's reputation—not me. In fact I admired Wairimu and always saw her as one of my daughters."

That was the famous, beautiful Wairimu. Wairimu the envied, the worshipped, the cherished village belle. The ideal wife for every man, old and young, and the daughter-in-law every mother dreamt of. Yet Wairimu the hated, the despised, and the most deserted girl in the village. And now, as Wambui was her best friend and had, due to her father's warning, deserted her, she had taken refuge in her distant aunt's village—thus trying to lead a new, lonely life and to forget her misfortunes and the bitterness she had borne. It was all a matter of misunderstanding. Nobody was there to explain. For those were the days when she, Wairimu, was only a child; when her mother was only a poor, unknown woman in the society, torn apart by calamities. But it happened, nevertheless.

For Ngigi, her father, was a born robber. And having been a robber since his youth, he had constantly disturbed the villagers by robbing them of their property. And now that he was old, the chance of him ever improving and being a decent villager was very small. So the elders gathered and after a long discussion they resolved that Ngigi should be taught manners. Ngigi, being the man he was, had heard about this through an unknown source, and had made off to the forest, where he lived, after renouncing his family, as an outcast. And there, having such a good hideout, his trade came in useful. He robbed all the more and manhandled women in such a way that he was damned by everyone. Ngigi was feared by everyone now. The women wouldn't go to the fields alone. The young boys couldn't herd the sheep alone for fear that Ngigi might steal one. And the more the people feared him, the more likely it was that he would be killed. Ngigi wouldn't live long. Something must be done, and quickly. So after the elders' meeting one night, sentence was passed on Ngigi, regardless of his family. The squad was formed and after equipping themselves in the proper manner they went out into the forest after Ngigi. And finally Ngigi was tracked down and the sentence passed on him was carried out. As a notorious robber, he deserved the robber's punishment—which he accordingly got. They put him in a beehive, took it to the top of a steep hill, and let it roll down to the bottom. And when it reached the bottom, they opened it, took him out and then wrapped him up in dry banana leaves which were eventually set alight—thus bringing an end to the notorious robber, restoring peace and teaching an unforgettable lesson to would-be robbers. And thus leaving Wairimu, an innocent child, fatherless. Being the daughter of a robber she led a hard, secluded life with no friend apart from her own mother. But, as luck would have it, she grew up through these hardships to be the centre of admiration, to be the envied village belle. This was the time when, due to her good behaviour and her beauty, she acquired a different reputation. And people began to see her from another point of view. The girls derived some kind of pleasure in her company. And the boys tried hard to win her, but beautiful Wairimu was invincible. Not that she hated them. Not that she was now retaliating, by vexing them after the hard life she had had. It was just that none of those boys appealed to her fancy. She laughed and joked with them, but knowing inside that one day the right boy would appear. And gradually he did.

She was coming from the river alone, carrying a jar of water on her back. As she came panting up the hill, wondering why the path was so deserted, she saw him, out of nowhere, standing in front of her—thus blocking her path. It was quite unexpected, quite unusual, but it happened nevertheless. He stood there, large as life, staring at her with a quiet appraisal. Wairimu felt herself tongue-tied and when he greeted her she just grunted confusedly. Her heart was thumping inside her as she tried with much shame to steal a glance at his face. He was in no better situation than her; he too was confused and shameful. But he was real—the man every girl talked about, the idolised hero. Why hadn't she thought about him before? Where was he anyway? In which part of her heart had she been keeping him all this long while? This, the most talked-about man in the whole village—the ideal hero for every woman. "Where are you going?" It was funny how she asked it as if it was her business. "To the river", he answered smiling, and revealing milk-white teeth. "Do you always go there?", she ventured again. "No, this is the first time." After that, fluent conversation followed, being punctuated by peals of laughter. And in the end, the conversation was concluded by an invitation from Nganga. She knew it was foolish to refuse such an invitation, but nevertheless a girlish instinct prompted her to appear disinterested. This was conventional. She was intending to show him that she was not after all so easy-going, and to give him the feeling that he was the chaser while she was the

chased, although she was not so sure that it was like that.
"I'll tell my sister Wambui to bring you home if
you're afraid", he persisted. He coaxed her slowly and
carefully, with much happiness, and in the end she
agreed and accepted his invitation. She was happy with
herself that she had not appeared "easy to crack", and
that she had not given him too hard a time. And when the
time of parting came, their eyes met and held each other,
and the language they spoke only the two of them could
understand.

Wairimu came home often after that, for it was natural
that Wambui took to her at once. Every time she came
home she found him there waiting for her. And together
they talked and laughed and encouraged each other.
Theirs was another world. A world of their own, a world
full of happiness and love. Every time they were together,
they felt carried away—away from everything—and they
were blind to everything around them. They sang to
each other, exchanged riddles, and told tales whose theme
was always people in love.

Then all of a sudden things changed and took a different
course. Wambui was warned by her father never to be
seen with Wairimu again. "Do you hear? I don't want her
in my compound again", the father warned her. "Her
father was a robber and she will soon start the people
here talking nonsense. I don't want her to spoil my good
reputation. Let her go in peace and try to forget her."

That evening her mother warned her too. It was hard
and incomprehensible. How could they bear a grudge
against a girl just because her father was a robber?
Wambui felt hurt and disappointed with her family.
Now she had to try to find a way to stop Wairimu from
coming home to see her. It was most extraordinary
because she felt she couldn't bring herself to tell Wairimu
the cause of it all. Nevertheless it had happened and she
had to act quickly, otherwise, if her father saw Wairimu
again in his compound, Fate only knew what he would
do. And what about Nganga, her brother? He would ask

questions. He would ask why Wairimu was not coming home. Had there been a row between the two girls? And if the answer was no, he would demand an explanation. He would give Wambui a hard time. All these and other questions would rise up later and they would all demand an answer from Wambui.

When she went to see Wairimu that evening, she was in a bad mood. But Wairimu so charmed her with her conversation and anecdotes that for a while she forgot what had really brought her there. And when the time to leave came, Wairimu escorted her and before they had parted Wairimu let it all out: "My mother and father have been quarrelling and everything at home is in a mess. I don't know what to do. Look, do me a favour. Will you stop coming home to see me for a while until everything has been settled? I'm sorry about this, but I can't help it. I want to be alone for a while." Wambui lied to her friend and when it was all over she felt free.

But Wairimu guessed the reason. How could the quarrel affect their friendship? How could Wambui tell her not to see her again so openly like that? And although she promised not to see Wambui again, Wairimu was hurt inside for she knew that her father's bad reputation had dealt her another blow. Wambui had been her best friend, and now that this had happened, she felt lonely again and disappointed with life. And this time she resolved to withdraw from the public and take refuge somewhere. She knew now that she was destined to such a life for ever. She would never have a true, reliable, girl-friend, much less a boy-friend. And so the next day she left her home for her distant aunt's village. There she would lead a different life and would try to forget her misadventures.

Nganga, after missing Wairimu for some time, began to wonder. He became restless. Food appeared tasteless to him. He felt lonely and hollow inside. He was always irritable and never spoke to anybody unless spoken to. He knew it now. There was no doubt about it. Love.

It was sweet and sour. When they were together it was sweet, wonderful and thrilling. Now he was alone, he couldn't see her anywhere; life was bitter and not worth living. He was deeply in love with Wairimu and he had to find her and let her know. He could never live without her. Wairimu was his body and his spirit.

On asking Wambui about Wairimu's absence, she gave incomprehensible answers which increased his anger all the more. He felt like beating her, but he dared not. How could people not care about Wairimu? How could they keep quiet like that when she was nowhere to be found? He took to hovering around her home in the hope that he might catch a glimpse of her by chance. Wairimu never appeared. He took to following all the paths he knew she would follow, but Wairimu had disappeared. Now people began to murmur. They started to talk about him. He would never get married, they said. Something must be wrong with him. Eligible girls were in plenty; his father was rich. It was just a question of proposing to a girl. His father would do the rest. What was wrong with him then? Was he afraid? Afraid of what? Of his not being a full, real, potent man? That was probably it.

One evening Nganga came home in a sore mood, after a futile search at Wairimu's home. He went straight to his father's hut. He was as irritable as a man in love would be. On entering, he grabbed a stool and sat on it. He knew that whatever he was about to say wouldn't please his father. Nevertheless, he felt that this was the time and place to break it to his father, and get it over with. Wairimu was still alive, there was no question of that, and she had not married or he would have heard about it. So he would get her sooner or later. "Father", he broke the silence, "I am getting married—to Wairimu, the daughter of Ngigi, so you had better be pre . . . ".

"What are you talking about? Are you mad, Nganga?", father asked, choking with anger.

"No, I am not mad, father", Nganga replied calmly.

"I love her and she loves me. If I can't get her as my first wife, no other girl will ever be my wife. So I thought you might as well ...".

"Stop it quickly, will you? What devil has got into you? Do you know who I am, to talk to me of a robber's daughter as your ... your bride?"

Nganga was already outside. His mind was made up and, above all, he had no time to argue with his father. He left and disappeared into the darkness.

Wairimu's mother, after hearing the "*hũti*" at the door, said "*ũka*"—come in—in answer to the visitor's call. She opened the door and welcomed the visitor with surprise. She had not expected a man to call on her, least of all Nganga. After the necessary greetings and introduction, Nganga asked her where Wairimu was. She didn't hesitate: she told him right away where her daughter had gone, and why she had gone there. "She was very lonely here and hopelessly miserable", she concluded. Nganga thanked her and, taking leave of her, went back to his hut. He took his sword, a club and a spear. Closing the door behind him, he left and disappeared into the darkness. The journey took him a day, and, when he finally arrived, he was led, after inquiring, to the hut he wanted. He called out "*hũti*", and a familiar, feminine voice answered him, "*ũka*". He entered and saw her. She was as beautiful as ever, but she had lost a few pounds now. She stood there, staring at him with surprise. She fascinated him and, likewise, he stood watching her like a picture. "Wairimu", he called, "are you well?" "Yes", she answered sweetly, "very well. And you?" Rather than answer, he smiled at her lovingly. "I love you, Wairimu." He broke down. She came to then. She dashed madly to him and embraced him hard. "Oh, Nganga, my love, my saviour, how I waited for you! I missed you, oh, how I ...". She broke down and sobbed on his massive shoulder. As she sobbed rhythmically, he listened lovingly. Then he began to sing to her:

"I left home, my love, in the middle of the night.
The children cried and the sheep bleated
But I left nevertheless,
With my sword and spear in hand.
I braved the night;
I descended the hills and crossed the rivers,
In pursuit of the beautiful one.
Now she is in my arms,
My love and my happiness,
Making my dreams come true.
When I take my beautiful home
The children will cry and the sheep will bleat
And Wairimu will be mine."

———————

After the food was ready, Wambui was sent by her mother to go and call her brother for his food. But after calling his name for a time, Wambui returned and told her mother that her brother wasn't in the hut. So the food was kept somewhere until he should come back home. The hours slipped away slowly and in the end the evening turned into the late hours of the night. But Nganga was nowhere to be found.

The night passed and the morning came. Wambui was sent again to check whether her brother had by any chance turned up. And when the answer was again "no", Wambui's mother prepared to go and break the news to her husband. On hearing the news, Njoroge was very shocked and afraid that his fears had come true after all, but he tried with success to control himself in front of his wife. "Go back to your hut; the boy will come home soon. He hasn't gone anywhere. He is around here somewhere." But he was not all that sure of himself.

As the morning gradually wore on, people began to be anxious. Njoroge was now growing furious and angry with everybody. Couldn't somebody do something to rectify the whole thing? How could it happen anyway? His son, Nganga, disappearing into thin air like that—

just like an object? It was all impossible, incredible, unbelievable.

When the afternoon began to draw to its close, Njoroge had entirely lost control of his temper. He was now scolding and reproaching everybody who happened to be near. He sent all of his wives and children to enquire about his son's whereabouts. And when the evening came and no news had been received, his anger turned into deep and bitter sorrow. He was now soaked with fear. His son must be somewhere. Something must have gone wrong with him. Wherever he had gone, he must have gone alone as nobody seemed to know anything about him. And why should he decide to go alone for such a long time to such an unknown place? He must have wanted some privacy—somewhere he was sure nobody would see him. And what was all this secrecy for? What was behind it all? To do something alone, no doubt. But something like what, for God's sake? There was only one answer to the mystery, Njoroge concluded. After their row the previous evening, Nganga had walked out of the hut like a wounded animal. He had approached his father with a request, just like any other son would have done. But Njoroge had turned him down. He had curtly refused. He had refused to allow him to marry the only girl he loved. He had broken his heart. And Nganga, thus treated, bursting with anger and love, had resolved to end it all, to get it over with, there and then. He must have . . . have . . . . Tears streamed down his cheeks as he thought of his son's fate. His corpse must have been lying somewhere, naked under the hot sun and the cold night breeze, with his weapons beside it no doubt. That was it. That was the answer. Nganga was dead: he had killed himself.

Lying there in bed wrapped in sorrow, Njoroge thought about himself and his household. He was the cause of it all. He had allowed it all to happen and now that it had happened there was no going back and starting anew. People would blame him for it now. Soon the women would start gossiping; they would despise him. They would hate him. And the old men would soon start to avoid him. His home would then earn a different reputation and the glorious past would be forgotten. He would have no status in the society after having allowed his son to commit suicide. It was all over now. After that, life would not be worth living at all.

Then it all came home to him. At first came bit by bit. And when somebody outside, just in conversation, mentioned the name Wairimu, it all dawned on him. He called Wambui, his daughter, to him and sent her to go and ask Wairimu whether she had seen Nganga. Wairimu, more than anyone, must know where he was. He must have said goodbye to her—his love. And what if they had disappeared together? What if they had . . . together?

The report came that Wairimu had recently gone away to her aunt's village, and that Nganga had gone to Wairimu's home to inquire about her. So it dawned on Njoroge then; all of it. He called some elders who had already gathered to console him, and sent them after his son with instructions that they should persuade him to come home if they happened to see him. "Tell him to come home. Tell him I have changed my mind and he can come home and have his wish. He is forgiven."

So the elders left for the village yonder. And they had hardly gone a mile from home when they saw two people approaching them from afar. The two were walking slowly, hand in hand, proudly, majestically, as if the whole world was theirs. It was hard to mistake the couple.